Design by www.breathebrandworks.com

Welcome to Health and Self-Care. This is a journey; a journey through some of the unwritten curriculum of life. Together, we will look at topics not usually covered in the medical, nursing or other curricula, but which we have found important for ourselves - often the hard way, from experience.

You bring your excellent professional skills as you help care for people and move forwards into the future. Your role involves teamwork, leadership and communication; supporting the values and vision of our health care system with your values and vision. But, as they say in the safety announcements on the aeroplane:

"Put on your own oxygen mask before assisting others."

We want you to succeed to the best of your ability, so have put together this booklet of tips and information for staff. It contains ideas and models, tips and advice - some of which may be obvious, some not, some familiar to you and some new. The booklet consists of wisdom and advice from experienced doctors and from elsewhere in life. We are privileged to be able to share this with you and try to build a fence at the 'cliff edge'.

When we practice the art of medicine, we reconnect to the heart of medicine.

So what's in the booklet?

It's an overview of the non-medical 'soft' thoughts that make life go well for each of us - a short guide to 'what makes us tick and how to tick better', designed for all staff. It contains advice on pitfalls, challenges and what to do when you're stuck, with suggestions from a number of authors. We look at the gaps in what we have learnt, from Investing in the Bank of Health, to the Drama Triangle which can exhaust us, as well as Top Tips for being a Patient, or looking after other Health Professionals who are patients. What's more, we look at issues of health which affect both Hardware Body and Software Being. Some of it comes from popular psychology, some aims at maturity of wise approach and some is very practical. Some is a bit out of the ordinary – but, we hope you'll agree, of interest.

Who cares for the carers? Nobody, if we don't at least care for ourselves.

Namaste is an old Eastern greeting meaning 'I salute the Divinity within you'.

Your Vision and Values

Kindness supports. Criticism withers.
Positive Thinking is an incredibly powerful force for good…
The only certainty about Life is that Change is always present.

Optimism is infectious. Cheerfulness irradiates. Compassion is infectious.

As a Health Professional - whether consultant, family doctor, junior doctor, matron, ward sister, staff nurse, receptionist, health care assistant, physio, occupational therapist, secretary, admin, catering department, switchboard, maintenance or services - we are all leaders, but we are not on our own; there is always help and support around, as long as we ask. Lao Tsu said:

"The leader knows that the task has been accomplished and all is done, when the people say "we did it"."

We each have a vision for our lives, our job, our department and our health system. This is really important, and will help everyone to go forwards. Do think about your vision carefully and nurture it. Take care to align it with the System's vision and values, even if this involves helping develop a vision for the area you are an expert in. Does your vision align with the values of the organisation?

Remember that time spent in reconnaissance is never wasted. Find out what has been done before; find out what others think; don't waste the energy of your idea in idle gossip but do discuss it with peers. Remember that a vision solidified on paper has more power than just ideas in a head and that people take on board new ideas in different ways:

- Some (auditory) need to hear it
- Some (visual) need to see it
- Some (kinaesthetic) need to imagine and feel it

So our actions and our communication should cover all these angles (or at least, find out how the person you're communicating with learns best). Remember we are dealing with people and, while some have fragile or prickly egos (often from inner fear), some others feel secure and supported, and thus radiate greatness. One friend found that a 'Draft proposal' with no name went much further than an idea trumpeted out, especially at the stage of gathering support and moulding an idea, listening to feedback, and understanding other people's point of view.

It is well worth building up capital in relationships. This often leads to positive communication and success for both parties. Remember every person is guided by 'best intention' (though not always obvious, and sometimes heavily influenced by self-interest).

Values

What are your values? What are the values of the team and organization? Gratitude and compassion, care, respect, excellence, adaptability, integrity, accountability and transparency are all worth considering.

Respect, compassion and gratitude are possibly the most powerful values to ensure long term health of a person and organization. At Her Majesty's Prison Guy's Marsh, Dorset, there is a large Notice:

"The Number One Rule: try to treat others as you wish to be treated yourself"

So what are the important values in an organization? Organizations can be like families, with relationships, interactions, and growth opportunities (and sometimes tensions and upsets). This poem below helps to highlight some of the key family values.

Family Values

We are each a part of the human family (and in turn, each part of life's family of animals, vegetable and mineral kingdoms).

There are certain values we would aspire to learn but are not necessarily taught. These include but are not limited to:

- Love and Compassion
- Respect for self and others, and for all life
- Patience and Inner Peace
- Faith in Life
- Hope and Humility
- Gratitude
- Boundaries
- Right use of power
- Courage
- Being present
- Being grounded
- Manifesting our will

A Family is...

A family is a deeply rooted tree with branches of different strengths, all receiving nourishment from an infinite source

A family is where character is formed, values are learned, ethics created and society preserved

A family is where all members contribute and share, cooperate and work, and accept their responsibilities toward the good of the group

A family is where holidays are celebrated with feasting, birthdays acknowledged with gifts, and thoughts of days gone by kept alive with fond remembrances

A family is where each can find solace and comfort in grief, pleasure and laughter in joy, and kindness and encouragement in daily living

A family is a haven of rest, a sanctuary of peace, and most of all, a harbour of love

Anon

Absence of any one is expressed by the Latin word 'sine', Spanish 'sin', which means 'without'.

Without can mean 'waiting outside' or 'waiting to come in'.
So sin is a state of waiting to come back in - a state of separation, waiting to be reunited and made whole again - to be welcomed back into the 'family of life'. This includes the 'whole of life', all of nature and creation. Otherwise we are just clever human beings who see themselves as separate from the

‘whole’; self-importantly seeking pleasure to avoid our unfulfilled needs. ‘Connection’ is one of our deepest needs. Connection to others, to family, friends, and strangers; connection to nature, to the world we live in, and to life itself. When we feel, and know, that we are ‘connected’, we can then take joy and fulfilment in this relationship.

We each need to have a ‘philosophy of life’ that works for us, involving faith and hope, a purpose and a vision. In order to work these out, we need to think about the subject, and listen carefully to the wisdom ‘life’ offers us. We need to cultivate ‘inner peace’ to achieve this. That way, we can be enjoy life’s journey aligned to our potential as, from Inner Peace springs Effective Action (IPEA).

Doctor’s D’s

Ask a hundred people how they are, and what do they say? “FINE” otherwise put as Feelings Inside Not Expressed. So everyone uses **Denial**. Ask a hundred health professionals, mothers, managers or others with responsibilities how they are - they don’t answer because they’re too busy with their concerns! This is **Displacement**. So health professionals are heavily defended against looking after their own health (own oxygen mask), and fall into patterns of disharmony and imbalance.

Fearful
Insecure
Neurotic
Emotionally Imbalanced

The two D’s of **Denial** and **Displacement** may lead into the three Ds of **Drink**, **Drugs** and **Depression** - on the way visiting the other D’s of **Distress**, **Despair**, **Disillusionment, Divorce**, **Debt** and **Discipline**. Tragically, this may end up with the final D of **Death**.

“*Anti-ideal*” as some would say. But if we choose to drive on a road with no map or idea of the territory we may inevitably get lost and into difficulties. The moral of the story is that if we learn about the territory *and* take appropriate care, we are much more likely to have a smooth and successful journey - free from problems!

Reflection points:

- Are you good at caring for yourself?
- What are your values?
- Are you at peace within yourself?
- Who is your ‘family’?
- Do you feel ‘connected’?
- How might you achieve and maintain ‘connection’?
- How might you achieve ‘inner peace’?

We each have a current account in the '**bank of health**'.

We start with an inherited positive balance. Other people invest in us as we grow, with kindness and other acts to help our health.

We make our own deposits daily, with high quality sleep, friendships, exchanges of kindness, breathing harmoniously, acting in line with the 'flow of life', eating high vitality foods, drinking vibrantly healthy water, supporting our nutrition with herbs, doing T'ai Chi or Yoga and nourishing our soul with music, compassion, time in nature, and doing what we love.

We all make sure we put fuel in the tanks of the cars we drive and ensure that our income goes into our bank account. So we can do this for our own health too!

We may make deposits in each of the following: the 'physical account', the 'emotional account', the 'mental account' and the 'spiritual account'. In this way, we build up 'capital'.

We use up energy daily from the 'bank of health' on various activities. Sometimes we squander this energy profligately and spend a whole lot at once on a fruitless time wasting activity. Sometimes we deplete it slowly, eroded by poor sleep, too long on devices, ingesting artificial additives or sweeteners, chemicals, or devitalized and over-processed food which looks far from the nature it came from. We may use our bodies badly, with poor posture, little joy and bad habits.

Often we fail to notice that on a daily basis we may be spending more than we deposit. The long-term effect of this has to be that our credit balance moves steadily towards overdraft and illness…

We all have choices and choices have consequences…

Regular savings build up a fund of capital, will yield well and stand us in good stead for the future!

Let's just make a deposit into the 'bank of inner calm'!

Please put both feet on the ground; allow your spine to become upright and comfortable. Feel free to allow yourself to take three slow abdominal (diaphragmatic) breaths - slowly in and out. Notice how you feel - you have just introduced 'calm' into your body. Feel free to repeat this whenever you wish…

Reflection points:

- What changes might you consider in your life from now?
- What is it that you already know that you need to do next?

03.1 Wheel of Life

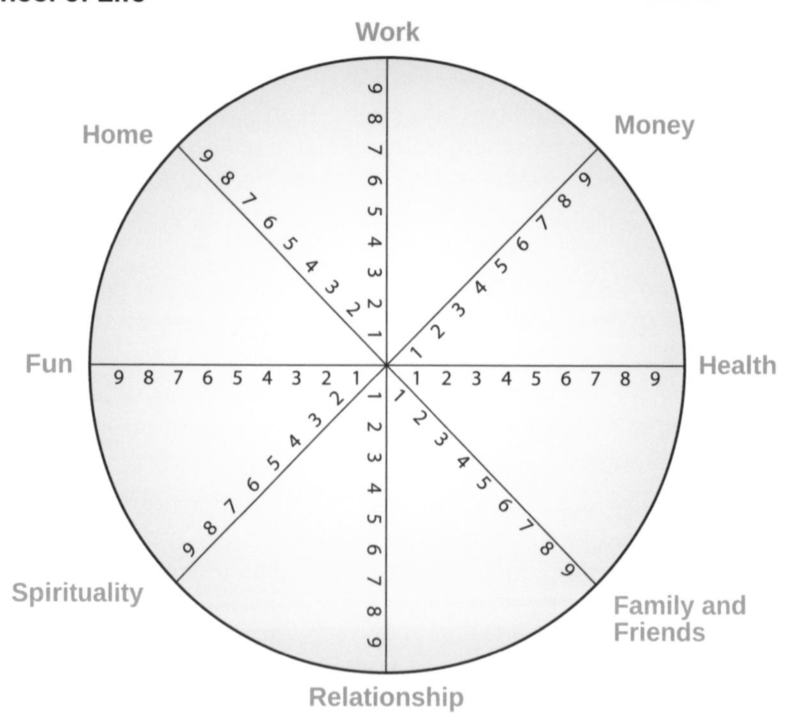

Thanks to Dr Sarah Coope.

The Wheel of Life is a simple tool to help us work out how things are and how we would like them to be! Simply put a dot, on a scale of 1-10, where you estimate your current situation to be. Then join the dots! This is your current state of being in your life.

You can vary this wheel - although we suggest: work; home; relationships; spirituality; family and friends; health; fun and money.

You could also have hobbies, feeling of purpose, feeling valued or any other area you feel important.

Next, you may wish to think about your ideal work-life balance - and how would your wheel of life look then? (hint: fill in the dots for this ideal and look at how the wheel looks)

- How will you get from the present to your ideal?
- What small steps can you make towards the ideal?
- What changes do you need to make?

Dr. Robin Philipp, Consultant Occupational and Public Health Physician, UHBristol NHS Trust, 2016.

The saying: *"Do unto others as you would have them do to you"*, is built into many philosophies, faiths and religions. It can be traced back to Socrates and is implicit in professionalism, any profession and the six core values of the NHS Constitution: working together for patients; respect and dignity; commitment to quality of care; compassion; improving working lives; and everyone counts.

In 2012, similar values were incorporated as the 6 C's in Compassion in Practice Nursing, Midwifery and Care Staff: our vision and strategy, published by the Department of Health and NHS Commissioning Board: care; compassion; competence; communication; courage; and commitment. Since 2014, all NHS healthcare staff have been expected to embrace and adhere to these core values. They are the principles on which standards of behaviour are based and judged. They show patients, colleagues, visitors and the public that we respect them and care about the care we give. These core values are similar to those identified by the British Medical Association in 1994 for the medical profession in the 21st Century. They were described by the BMA as: *"the 'ancient virtues of competence, integrity, confidentiality, compassion and commitment practised with an enquiring and impartial mind"*.

Irrespective of who we are or what we do, showing that we care imparts a sense of hope to people in need of our help. It also has a personal payback. After all, having pride in what we do and our commitment to how we go about doing it is reflected in the appreciation and gratitude of patients and colleagues and lessens the likelihood of complaints. This in turn boosts our morale and self-respect and leads us to a sense of achievement and personal satisfaction in a job well done. These feelings help to strengthen our coping skills and benefit our overall resilience in dealing with the day-to-day pressures at work.

In essence then, being kind, considerate and supportive of other people pays huge dividends for the people we care for and about, and also for each of us. These qualities are inherent components of our professional and personal integrity. 'Integrity' is the quality of being honest, sincere and having a sense of what is right and proper in one's conduct. It's worth reflecting too that as the poet John Donne wrote way back in 1624 in his Meditation XVII, *"No man is an island, entire of itself"* or, putting this another way: *"everything in life is connected"*. Reaching out to others and being there for each other is in essence part of what it means to be human.

There is with this a time-honoured saying that sets out the key message:

"We get back in life what we give out". The word 'compassion' sums up for us what at all times is needed.

'Self-compassion' is a component of this need: 'taking care to ensure that as well as caring for others we care for ourselves'. It's about being kind to ourselves, giving ourselves time and treating ourselves with love, care, dignity and self-respect. It's also about being in the present moment, accepting and non-judgemental when encountering pain and personal shortcomings, and accepting of these feelings. This requires taking a balanced approach to one's negative emotions so that feelings are neither accepted nor exaggerated. Instead it's about observing them within and with openness so that they are held in 'mindful awareness'; a non-judgemental, receptive state in which individuals observe their thoughts and feelings as they are without trying to suppress or deny them. Properly learned and applied it can be an effective tool to reduce stress and enhance one's wellbeing.

In 1999, the Nuffield Trust used these points and the Concept of Reciprocal Maintenance: 'We need to look after the things that look after us', to help explore relationships between the art and science of medical practice and the importance of developing a renewed interest in the medical humanities. They were defined as: 'the study of human nature and the practice of compassionate concern for the welfare of mankind'. The term 'humanities' comes from the Latin word 'humanitas', used, Wikipedia tells us, by Cicero (106-43 BC) *"in describing the formation of an ideal speaker who he believed should be educated to possess a collection of virtues of character suitable for an active life of public service and a decent and fulfilling private life"*. He added, in advice to his brother, that : *"if fate had given you the authority over Africans or Spaniards or Gauls, wild and barbarous nations, you would still owe it to your humanitas to be concerned about their comforts, their needs and their safety"*.

'Compassion' was defined in this work with the Nuffield Trust as: 'having a sympathetic understanding of suffering and distress and a desire to help alleviate it'.

In 2012, 'compassion' was reported similarly by the UK Department of Health and the NHS Commissioning Board in their renewed vision and strategy for nursing practice. They noted it to be: *"how care is given through relationships based on empathy, respect and dignity - it can also be thought of as intelligent kindness and is central to how people perceive their care"*.

From these definitions, 'compassionate care' was described in 2015 for the University Hospitals Bristol NHS Foundation Trust Working Group on Compassion in Care as: "attention in life and living to the giving of understanding, support, advice and reassurance that helps to foster health and wellbeing".

In thinking about the need to show compassion and give compassionate care in the NHS, a staff member of UHBristol NHS Trust expressed recently to the Working Group in an anonymous, concise, straightforward and somewhat poetic way that:

"Compassion is…

Treating someone as you would wish to be treated,

listening without judging and

doing your best in every interaction."

Cicero, in defence of using poetry and literature in this sort of way, stated in a famous speech that: "These studies sustain youth and entertain old age, they enhance prosperity, and offer refuge and solace in adversity; they delight us when we are at home without hindering us in the wider world, and are with us at night, when we travel and when we visit the countryside".

The rhythms, cadence and images of poetry continue to be used to help express and share feelings and our understanding of compassion; they add impact and appeal to what is being said and done and help us to better enable hope for a more positive outcome from the care we give. These qualities make poetry an excellent medium for expressing and sharing feelings as to what compassion means, how we can show it and why it matters to us all in life and living - not only in the giving and receiving of healthcare. The poem, 'Compassion Deserves Concern' attempts to illustrate what we can do with compassion as a tool and with resultant personal, patient and organisational gain:

Compassion deserves concern

1

Compassion deserves concern
It's a kind of kindness
Something precious shared
It's in the what of what it is
That matters much
In the care we care about
A value
That we value;

2

This compassion
It is something found
And in us all
A kindness felt and thought
There to share
Enjoyed as time well spent
In how we say and go about
All it is we do;

3

It is with compassion
We show we can
And do with care
In our care
Take care
To show we care
And that it is for all
For whom we care;

4

It is there
In a gentle touch
A listening ear
A friendly
Warming word
An engaging smile
A shared moment
A reaching out;

5

Given and received
To comfort and reassure
Support to be enjoyed
That's all it takes
To make a difference
And let it be known
It is with you we are
It's you we care about;

6

Compassion shows
We understand
And that with it
If our care is for you
It is just as if
if we were you
We would wish
You with us to be.

In conclusion, the art of medical practice or, in other words, how we go about doing what we do, plays a big part in ensuring successful clinical outcomes from the treatment and care we give. Showing compassion and delivering compassionate care can make a big difference, at no extra cost. It benefits us as well as our patients, colleagues, visitors and more generally, the public. Compassion is therefore a quality that deserves more attention. It assists social cohesion and is worth valuing and holding on to as a core value, adhering to it in everything we do. It's something that's worth thinking about more and applying consistently in the care we give ourselves and show in support of other people and our NHS as an organisation. It's a win-win tool.

See also Compassion in Healthcare 2, section 30 (p164).

Health is harmony of mind, body and spirit, not just the absence of disease.

Health is defined as:

"A state of complete physical, mental and social well-being and not merely the absence of disease or infirmity." WHO 1948

Health is when we are at our ease (not 'dis-eased') and when we have harmonious relationships. Health is harmony and vitality of both 'hardware body' and 'software being' as well as their interaction with each other. Health is characterised by harmony, not discord; by smooth emerging patterns, not by disordered jangly ones.

> If we separate illness from health,
> health from life and life from living,
> we deceive ourselves,
> and conspire to create the
> falsehood of a reality which is not.
> *Anon.*

Long-term health includes our pathway and journey through life. Life's path unfolds in the now, building upon the capital of the past, and developing in life with the dreams and imagination of the future. Life is a journey of personal development towards maturity and wisdom, and towards a fusion of our individual 'ego' with our highest potential.

Each of us has an 'ego' that starts life living on the ground floor (or stage), whilst the potential is at a higher level, guiding us to emerge like a series of fractal patterns. They say that coincidence is God's way of remaining anonymous. In reality, life manifests events and happenings through our experience as resonant possibilities coincide, and the potential manifests into reality.

The word Heal-th comes from the Anglo-Saxon 'Hale', meaning: whole, robust, vigorous, and relates to being whole, complete and full of vitality, and in balance. Psychological health, as conscious beings, includes self-awareness and self-knowledge.

On the portico of the Greek Temple at Delphi were the two sayings:

- **Γνωθι σεαυτον** **Know Thyself**
- **Μηδεν αγαν** **Everything in Moderation; Everything in Balance**

Nature evolves according to patterns of harmony; we find fascinating patterns of geometry as pictures emerge, such as the Golden Mean: $\frac{1+\sqrt{5}}{2}$

This has an underlying connection to the Fibonacchi Ratio, as seen in the seed-head of a sunflower or in the ratios of sacred geometry in nature, cathedrals and elsewhere.

CC Pixabay

CC Valtercirillo Pixabay

The important relationships to have in balance or in harmony are:

1. With ourselves and how we live our lives
2. With our relationship to our own body (the vehicle for our conscious self)
3. With our relationship to others (other conscious beings)
4. With our relationship to and interaction with Nature
5. With our interaction with our environment
6. With our relationship to, and understanding of, Life
7. Our connection to the Wonder and Energy of Life

So, do we wish to have kindness in these relationships or criticism and negativity?

LKS - Love and Kindness Supports, CW - Criticism Withers, (LKSCW)

If you are really healthy, you are bursting with vitality, energy and engagement in the flow of life.

Our 'hardware body' is made up of our blood, bones, muscles, organs, pumps, pipes, pulleys and electric cables, and cellular function. Our 'software being' is an electromagnetic body (all cells produce electricity and electromagnetic fields; heart cells are especially strong). We need to learn about keeping our 'software being' healthy as well as our 'hardware body'.

Who cares for the carers?
Only we can for ourselves. Remember, the airlines tell us to secure our own oxygen mask first before helping the person next to us.

Self-care means learning about and paying attention to Health. Not just taking it for granted until illness comes along! We each have a responsibility to ourselves to take this seriously.

Self-care is not selfishness, it is vital for our long-term health and survival. We can postpone our own needs for a while but they always come back to us, so it's better to be proactive.

Health is harmony of **body**, **mind** and **being**. Deviation from health leads us into illness, so it's worth being pro-active and learning about health:

Connect, be active, take notice, learn and give[1]

Nourish your **body** - get sleep, exercise, fresh air, sunlight and great food. A car that you don't service and put the wrong fuel into runs badly, if at all. Dance, sing or laugh sometimes! High quality nutrition is key. Avoiding maintenance is an unhealthy choice to make, just like avoiding the washing-up in the kitchen is also unhealthy. Remember: choices have consequences!

Learn how to still your **mind** and use it carefully An overactive, clever mind can drive you into difficulties. Learn mindfulness, reflection or anything else that works for you. Remember: garbage in, garbage out. So connect to beauty and nature, don't just watch electronic screens. 'Mindfulness' is a powerful tool to learn for life.

Being. Spirituality is everyone's natural connection, with the wonder and energy of life and the instinct to explore that experience and its meaning. It is connecting to our faith, purpose and philosophy, and in a conscious co-creative universe, it's like using a Satnav to guide us to our destination; the Life We Were Each Born To Live (LWWBTL).

[If this concept sounds a bit airy-fairy, or feels uncomfortable, please just read about Six System Problems, p30.]

Spirituality affirms that personal development is about the growth of compassion and consciousness, heart and mind.

Take time to think about what really matters to you in life: your 'core values'. If you use these to guide you, harmony can flow. If you try and act in conflict with your values, life will give you a lesson.

And remember: every day is a school day (EDASD). We are all always learning!

Even more: Everyone is My Teacher (EIMT). We can and do learn from everyone and everything in life. Every Day has a new lesson – the Unwritten Lesson Plans of Life (ULPL).

Our challenge is to recognise the patterns and meaning that are hidden everywhere.

> Where is the Life we have lost in living?
> Where is the wisdom we have lost in knowledge?
> Where is the knowledge we have lost in information?
> *TS Eliot, The Rock*

Health for Health Professionals, in more depth.
'Health' means 'soundness of body' or 'a condition of wholesomeness' and comes from the root 'heal-th'. Heal means to restore to health, to cure (a person of a disease); to make whole or healthy and is derived from the same word that means hale or whole. Thus we find the idea of completeness rather than something missing, lacking or wounded.

Perhaps as health professionals we all carry wounds? Like Chiron, the 'Wounded Healer' (a centaur, half man, half horse) of Greek mythology, we seek not just to help our patients, but secretly (often unknown to ourselves) we are trying to heal our own wounds? Furthermore, the deepest wounds may not be physical, but invisible psychological ones.

How many people leave, after seeing a health profesional, glowing with health? We all want our patients to get better, but studied disease, not health. We learnt how to repair cars after crashes - not how to drive wisely and maintain the car in the first place.

Vis Medicatrix Naturae is an important and overlooked factor in health. The design default of the body is 'vibrant health', given the right conditions. A tree's bark will heal if cut, our bruises heal, cuts in the skin mend, and fractures (aligned correctly) unite. The design default of the body is self-repair. VMN means Vis: power or force, Medicatrix: healing, and Naturae: of nature. So it is nature's own (self) healing power. This depends upon both internal and external factors: nutrition, infection, and physical and emotional environment.

Farmers who look after animals spend a great deal of time and effort getting the nutrition and housing right for their stock. (I remember less than a day on nutrition in the medical curriculum). Interestingly, older farmers can tell stories about sick animals which go and eat particular plants in the hedgerow and then get better, thus choosing their own herbal medicine.

Doctors, however, have minimal control over what our patients choose to eat and whether it makes them healthy or not. This is a major problem and an important project; a learning need for society and physicians.

Now, looking at computers and all electronic equipment, we find that they all have both hardware and software components:

Computer = Hardware + Software

If you think of our bodies as the hardware, then our thoughts and feelings, which are invisible, are the part of the software. Some people would say that our mind is the computer by which our thinking is done, and that there is also something else which is personal to each of us. Down the ages the words soul and spirit have been used as shorthand to describe this something else, as in the phrase:

"And take not thy holy spirit from us". Book of Common Prayer, 1662

Hardware Body, Software Being (HWB, SWB)

In Eastern thinking in India and China, mind body and spirit are seen as interconnected, with man standing as a bridge between heaven and earth. This view is not held in Western civilization, starting with Greek philosophers, who separated body and mind. In the 1500s, as scientists became interested in the body, they asked the establishment (the Medieval Catholic Church) for permission to dissect the body. Permission was given, on condition they did not touch the soul.

So, for several centuries medical science has investigated the hardware of the body right down to molecular and electron microscope level but not looked at the software. Psychology is a comparatively young science, and much of it has been concerned with the mechanics of mind. (Applied energy psychology such as Emotional Freedom Therapy has been developed by therapists outside current university research.)

In Western tradition, some of our greatest thinkers have considered the position. It was Leonardo da Vinci who stated in 1499 that:

"By the law of the Almighty
The body is the work of the soul
Which fashions its outward appearance
By hammering it from within
Like a goldsmith embosses his material."

James Oschman[2] explains how our bodies are bodies electronic as well as electric.

He shows how meridians of energy (Chinese acupuncture theory) are actually information superhighways in the body, working along hydrated fascia, composed of crystal-like collagen; a bit like the information flows across a silicon chip.

Insights from physics have helped Information Technology that we all rely upon to produce the wonders of devices for instant communication: phones, computers and so on. Their hardware is based on chemistry and physics, and their software is based on physics. Current early 21st Century Medicine in the Western model is firmly rooted in chemistry, down to molecular structure, from the narrative of pathology, through anatomy and physiology, most diagnostics, to pharmacology and therapeutics. Current medicine largely ignores physics, except for CT and MRI scans and the IT

05.1 Chakras, Indian Culture

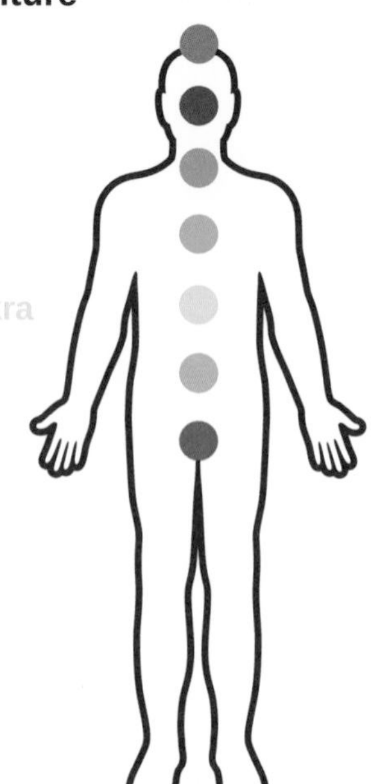

05.2 Meridians of information, Chinese Culture

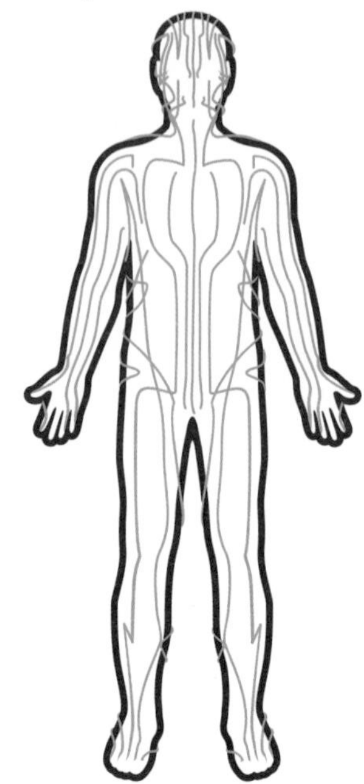

Curiously, there may be a relationship between Maslow's Hierarchy of Needs and the Chakras.

used at work. In doing this, Medicine not only misses a trick, it holds back its own natural evolution into adding the use of informational harmony to all current practices.

Indeed, much of Western biomedicine is based on reductionism, which ignores the wholeness of the mind-body-spirit philosophy of older wisdoms[3]. As healing is restoring harmony to the whole, Western medical philosophy , unless it evolves, is tragically doomed to fail some of the needs of patients, due a system problem, despite the best efforts of healing practitioners.

Perhaps the spirit is 'who the person really is' or the 'essence of a person'. After all, everybody's bodies are more or less similar (blood, bones, organs, hair, teeth, brain, heart and so on). Structurally our minds may also be similar but what makes each of us unique is the person we are? Maybe the spirit that moves through us?

Health is the other end of the spectrum from illness and doesn't happen by accident. To paraphrase Einstein:

"Health does not happen by itself, it requires understanding and effort".

Fortunately, the default setting for human bodies and minds is to become healthy again: wounds heal, fractures mend, the immune system works, cells regenerate - given the right conditions!

If everything is in balance, we feel 100% vibrant and healthy.

Lack or less of any of these cuts the 100% down to 90, 80, 70 or less. Patients often only go to see their doctor with non-specific tiredness or other complaints when health is at maybe 60%, whilst serious health issues may involve a drop even lower. (Obviously this is not a model for serious acute infections, infarctions, fractures or genetic illnesses, but it has its uses).

Even worse, many of us in society are just a teeny bit lazy, and we want a quick fix, hence:

'You're well until you're ill, then see the doctor for a pill.'

Of course, this approach, like driving a car without ever checking fuel, oil or water levels, or doing other maintenance, is likely to have adverse consequences. Paying attention to health can bring great dividends!

As the old pop song went:

"Accentuate the positive [health], eliminate the negative [illness]."

Johnny Mercer, 1944

Remember: health is harmony of **body**, **mind** and **being** and it doesn't happen by accident!

Good health depends upon:

- Good quality sleep (early enough in the night to ensure good melatonin production)
- Fresh air and sunlight (vitamin D)
- Water
- Interaction with nature (nature nurtures us)
- Exercise (our bodies are designed to move)
- Food (and herbs) of high quality (the design default was roots, shoots, nuts, fruit, raw meat, animal and vegetable fat and spring water. However, cooking and preserving have changed things, let alone the introduction of wheat 10,000 years ago, and food manufacturing in the 20th and 21st centuries)
  Dr Sarah Myhill[4] states that our bodies have experienced hundreds of thousands of years of a hunter-gatherer diet, ten thousand years of a glucogenic diet, and 150 years of a glucotoxic regime.
- Correct balance of nutrients and trace elements
- Freedom from heavy metal toxicity: aluminium, mercury (dietary, industrial and therapeutic sources), arsenic and others
- Environment free from harmful chemicals and electromagnetic fields (aspartame breakdown products include methanol, which is metabolised to formaldehyde, a neurotoxin and Class 1 carcinogen)
- Living in the now, free from worries of the past or future
- Emotional balance
- Social interactions
- Purpose (fulfilling the pattern of the life you were born to live)
- Mastery of skills that support purpose
- A degree of autonomy to live your life yourself (not following someone else's agenda)

Health professionals learn a lot [to use a metaphor] about car crashes - but they learn very little about wise driving, car maintenance, traffic flow or road design. Surely driving well and looking after our 'vehicles' can help us navigate through life rather better - driving carefully, avoiding car crashes, and avoiding running out of fuel!

Reflection points:

- What have you learnt to apply to your own health?
- What might you investigate further?

Introduction

"Aspects of personal and colleague health, especially mental health, should be part of the curriculum for all medical students. Doctors must learn to provide themselves and their colleagues with the same level of excellent care that they provide for their patients."[1]

Doctors are an important resource for society and appreciable public resources are put into their training. The estimated cost of training a junior doctor in the United Kingdom is around £250 000, with further costs for postgraduate training.[2] Any loss of trained workforce due to avoidable ill health is a waste to the health service, a loss to patients, a stress on colleagues and a disruption to doctors' own careers.

However, doctors make bad patients, tending to underuse health services and present late for treatment. And doctors who see doctors and other healthcare professionals as patients may be tempted to treat them differently from other patients. In addition, there may be issues specific to healthcare professionals, such as the effect on their health of their fitness to practice.

When seeing fellow healthcare professionals (HCPs) as patients, it is important to:

- Have confidence in conducting a consultation with the same "rules" and expectations as any other patient.
- Be aware of, and avoid the pitfalls of, treating them differently.
- Reflect on your own behaviour and role when consulting as a patient and understand the importance of taking care of your own physical and mental health.

Doctors as patients: understanding the problem

Doctors are at risk of the same illnesses as their patients, including acute or chronic conditions. However, they are also exposed to additional risks, such as catching infectious diseases from patients. In addition, doctors often seem to neglect their own healthcare, not taking up screening or immunisations as much as they could.

Some types of ill health are common in doctors - mental health problems in particular. Doctors as a group are high achievers, responsible, conscientious, driven, self-critical and self-doubting.[3] These traits in moderation are necessary in medicine, but when extreme, lead to significant anxiety and morbid preoccupation with having not done enough or having failed patients. Consequently, doctors have high rates of mental health problems, including anxiety, depression and addiction. Young female doctors are at higher risk of psychological distress, minor psychiatric disorders and specific mental health disorders.[4] The rate of suicide is higher than the general population and significantly higher than other professions such as lawyers.[5] It is particularly raised among female doctors, who are two and a half times more likely than other women to kill themselves.[6]

The reasons for doctors' failure to seek appropriate and timely help are multifactorial. Structural barriers, such as being unable to seek help during working hours, and frequent moves that make it difficult to register with a general practitioner, may mean doctors find it difficult to access services.[7] They also have problems accessing confidential help, among other professional concerns, including fear of affecting career progression and stigma about disclosing they have mental illness. Doctors are often reluctant to tell employers about mental health problems, and many do so only if this is a condition of employment. However, when doctors with mental health problems relinquish their medical self and become patients, the outcomes are good in terms of reduced distress and impairment and global improvement.[8]

In the face of the above anxieties, many doctors have either treated themselves or had informal ('corridor') discussions with colleagues. Informal consultation, with no clear lines of responsibility or action, leads to an increase in anxiety, which tends to exacerbate the situation. Doctor patients, particularly those with complex problems, may evoke a range of responses in the treating physician, ranging from bland reassurance to clinical overreaction, and thus they may end up with a poorer standard of treatment than the general patient.[9]

Numerous doctors have written about their experiences of becoming patients and how this has influenced their own practice. High profile examples include Dr Kate Grainger (who inspired the *#hellomynameis* campaign on Twitter) and Professor Kieran Sweeney. Key themes that come out of these accounts are not unique to being a healthcare professional: the importance of 'seeing the patient as a person' and good communication.

Illness can shatter doctor's professional identify where prevailing culture in medicine is one where doctors are considered to be 'invincible'.[1] Wessely and Gerada observe:

"The nature of doctors' training results in a deep rooted sense of being special and the institutionalisation of their professional identity, with the creation of a medical self that… allows doctors to do their job effectively, when they have to deal with stressful and long hours, and provides the veneer of invincibility to live and work in such close proximity with sickness." [10]

These characteristics, however, also distort doctors' ability to seek help and adopt the role of patient. For example, when accompanying a relative or friend to hospital, doctors often find it hard to relinquish their professional role and be the concerned 'lay person'. Abandoning their medical self is challenging, even in the short term. This dissonance might also explain why doctors are able to sacrifice their personal, social, financial, and often spiritual lives at work, remaining there long beyond what would be considered safe for themselves or their patients."

When sick, healthcare professionals find it difficult to take time off work ('presenteeism'). A study in Finland found that more than a third of doctors and nurses go to work despite feeling that they should have taken sick leave, whereas only a quarter took time off work for health reasons. Doctors worry about the disapproval of their medical colleagues and have to deal with their own feelings of guilt and shame.[1] A sick doctor can also pose a direct risk to patients and may give suboptimal care owing to excessive work demands and burnout.

Doctor-healthcare professional consultations

When a doctor does become a patient, consultations are difficult to negotiate, especially where mental health is concerned. This scenario is more challenging because the clinician whom the doctor sees would previously have been viewed as a colleague, but is now 'acting outside' this framework. Doctors who become patients often try to regain control of their medical self during consultations by talking shop to reassert their medical self.

There is little research to guide how doctors, on both sides of the fence, should behave but the GMC and BMA provide some helpful guidance. The underlying principle is that a doctor's first concern is the patient, and doctors who happen to be patients are entitled to the same high standards of care.

Doctors should avoid the temptation to take short cuts or make assumptions: doctor-patients should be offered the same explanations of what is involved in the investigation and management of their condition. They may already be well aware of such information but should be allowed the opportunity to be the patient and be offered advice and support, if they want that, as other patients would be. They may be much better informed than most other patients and their special knowledge should be recognised, without assumptions being made about the amount of information and detail they want. They should be reassured that seeking formal medical care is the right decision, rather than relying on their own interpretation of their condition. They should be encouraged to develop a continuing relationship with their doctor, including routine recall for follow up.

Guidance from the GMC[11] and BMA[12] on treating patients who are doctors:

- Doctors need to monitor their own health and not be reluctant to seek professional help. They have a responsibility to ensure that their health problems do not affect patient care.
- Doctors must comply with occupational health and safety requirements, including recommended vaccination and testing requirements.
- Doctors who think they may have been exposed to a serious communicable disease must seek and follow advice from a suitably qualified colleague, such as a consultant in occupational health, infectious diseases or public health, and, if found to be infected, have regular medical supervision.
- Doctors should avoid treating or prescribing for themselves, their family or close friends. They should be registered with a GP and consult their GP rather than deal with health problems alone or informally via colleagues. (The number of fitness-to-practise cases featuring allegations of self-prescribing, self-treatment or informal treatment of family and colleagues had increased from 36 in 2010 to 98 in 2012).
- Doctors who are patients have the same rights as other patients, including the right to confidentiality.† Only in exceptional cases, can the confidentiality of any patient be breached. Disclosure may be needed, however, if the individual puts others at risk.
- Doctors also have a duty to take action if they become aware that a colleague's health is affecting patient care.

†Out of area referrals may be an option in cases where the sick doctor has particular worries about confidentiality or fears that he or she is likely to be formally treated by colleagues who are acquaintances, which may lead to inadvertent disclosure of their information.

"Being a doctor does not exclude you from being a human being"

Dr Eleanor James, a consultant oncologist:

1. Eat, drink, wee, take time off. Being a doctor does not exclude you from being a human being.
2. You will not be able to be perfect 100% of the time. Being a doctor does not exclude you from being a human being.
3. Sometimes your colleagues will be nasty. Being a doctor does not exclude you from being a human being.
4. You will make mistakes. Being a doctor does not exclude you from being a human being.

5. You can't prioritise everything as most important. Some things just won't get done or won't get done very well. Being a doctor does not exclude you from being a human being.
6. You won't know how to do some things, or will be doing things you have never done before. This is scary but most of it's not that hard. You may just need to do it, but remember: being a doctor does not exclude you from being a human being.

Key points:

- Importance of maintaining confidentiality, and discussing and reassuring if necessary, perhaps offering non-local referrals if appropriate.
- Awareness of the emotional tumult described by doctors who suddenly become patients with a severe disease in the space of one consultation.
- Not assuming prior knowledge and explaining as you would to any other patient, taking cues from your patient as to how much understanding they already have about their condition and possible treatment.
- Addressing any potential difference in seniority between the doctor and patient: students and junior doctors may feel intimidated if they don't know answers to questions; acknowledge limits in knowledge and refer to colleagues if appropriate.

Further resources can be found in the reference section

Andrew suggests: It is remarkable that a profession that can be so compassionate and insightful into looking after the mental, emotional and physical needs of others, can often be blind to its own needs. It's as though caring for others can produce an 'insight deficit'. How is it that other professions with equally emotionally intense work (psychotherapists, counsellors and others) are mandated to have regular supervision (debrief/support) to ensure long term psychological integrity and health - and the medical profession is immune to this? We suspect 'insight deficit' which fortunately many are now addressing by accessing proactive support. (The root causes are denial and displacement, which lead to the other 'Doctor's D's' - see p8).

Specific problems that can also arise, compounded by lack of detachment, include Medical Narcissism (Banja), Medical Invincibility, and Adrenalism (addiction to endogenous adrenalin).

Barriers to Insight

Shame	Embarrassment
Fear of power loss	Fear of breach of confidentiality
Over-identifying with Role	Hidden curriculum of bravado and invincibility

So if there is a problem with health professionals as patients, are there some rules that would help us get it right? Prof Olaf Aasland, Norwegian Medical Association, Norway reminds us of healthy practice as a Patient and as a Physician.

Here are three sets of wise guidance:

Ten Top Tips for being a Patient (as a Doctor)

1. Ask for help in time - don't wait too long.
2. Consult another doctor other than yourself. AVOID self-medicating.
3. Ask the doctor to treat you as an ordinary patient. (Avoid the trap of clinging to the medical persona).
4. Be sure that this is a normal consultation with proper records kept, etc.
5. Ask the doctor for all the information and advice that she/he usually gives patients with the same illness.
6. No shortcuts. No 'corridor consultations'. If you are hospitalized, ask that ordinary routines and examinations be followed.
7. Do your best to follow the doctor's advice about sick-leave, diet, medication, etc. If you get little or no advice, be courageous and ask for it.
8. Inform your family and friends about your condition. (They will probably feel something is wrong.)
9. Inform your colleagues too, even if you are not on sick-leave. (Help destroy the myth that doctors can't get sick.)
10. Ask yourself why you got sick. Is there something in your lifestyle that should/can be changed?

Top Ten Tips for doctors who have colleagues as patients

1. The sick doctor is first and foremost a patient under your care. Treat the doctor-patient just like that.
2. Ensure open communication both ways between you and your doctor-patient, but remember he/she can be quite reduced by the illness.
3. Listen to the doctor-patient, but say clearly what you think are the best treatments, etc.
4. Do not leave it to the doctor-patient to make arrangements for examinations, tests, etc.
5. As with any other patient, write a case record, write prescriptions, and make an appointment for a return visit.
6. Do not hesitate to urge hospitalisation if you find it necessary. Follow your usual routine.

7. If the doctor-patient wants to be anonymous, not known as a doctor, respect this wish.
8. Give thorough information, not less than you usually give to your patients. Do not hesitate to repeat the information.
9. You are the one to make decisions as to when the doctor-patient should be discharged from the hospital, and when the sick-leave should end.
10. Remember: the doctor-patient is a person who is ill, (and no matter what their position may be in the medical hierarchy.) *You* are the doctor in charge.

Ten Top Tips for Doctors with Doctors as Parents of Patients

Contributed by Dr Paul Heaton, Consultant Paediatrician, Somerset UK

1. Assume total ignorance of facts, but maybe acknowledge they may have strong views upon the issue.
2. Don't pretend that you don't know they are doctors.
3. Don't use medical jargon.
4. Acknowledge that they do have some knowledge.
5. Be professional, but not over-familiar.
6. Establish what you want to be called, and how they would like to be addressed.
7. Don't be afraid to give them more 'scientific' information than you would to a non-medical person.
8. Don't assume that all is well from the perspectives of home life, money etc.
9. Sometimes it helps to be clear about exactly how are they 'medical'.
10. Abuse or neglect etc can (very rarely) still affect medical families.

Remember, as the professional, that you may sometimes have to play the role of scapegoat for patients or relatives who are unable to face up to the enormity of the issue that is in front of them. To help everyone move forward in this situation requires diplomacy and a clear understanding of the Drama Triangle (p78).

Reflection points:

- What experiences have you had when being a patient?
- What experiences have you had when being the professional to another health professional?
- Did you have any issues with either of these experiences?
- Which of the Ten Top Tips (top thirty!) resonate most with you?
- Does illness ever have a meaning?
- Can clouds sometimes have a silver lining?

One particular 'doctor's illness' to look out for is the picture of 'working too hard for too long at a high level of distress and misery' and thinking it is 'normal'...

A short philosophical diversion, as to why we can reject new ideas

"He was a real gentleman, honest to the core, willing to change his opinions and views once it was proved to him that he may have been wrong." Nathan Goldenberg

"Man trained to use hammer sees many things as a nail." Chinese proverb.

This section shows how some exploration of systems thinking may help people extricate themselves from cognitive and attitudinal traps that may be unconsciously held.

In 'life', there are both individual and system problems:

- Individual problem - single event, such as a car crash on a motorway.
- System problem - series of connected events, such as fifty car crashes on the same small section of motorway and none anywhere else.

System problems are notoriously difficult to discover and, even when discovered, just as difficult to resolve. You see, systems, like people, don't like criticism and don't like to admit problems (unless they have a learning and appreciation culture). Systems would sometimes rather 'shoot fifty messengers' than sort out the problem. Yet, in the motorway example above, it was only when it was analysed that they found the road surface to be poor, the road markings to be absent, the central barriers to be non-existent and three other factors. No wonder the individual car drivers had accidents. So are there any system problems in the way we look at life? They say that:

"There are no prison walls so powerful as those within our own minds"[1].

Here are six:
1. Not Invented Here (Give Up Your Thinking)
2. Insecure Ego (Give Up Your Power)
3. Mind-Body Split
4. Intuition Squashed
5. All Things are Connected (or not?)
6. The Paradox of Life - From Where do We Look at Life?

These main problems can be applied directly to health care.

1. Not Invented Here
'We didn't learn that at medical school, so it can't be true.' For instance, (my ego may say) nutrition, herbs, yoga, tai chi and use of acupuncture cannot be important for health because I didn't learn about them. There are no prison

walls so powerful as those inside our minds. *Give up your thinking*.

This simple device is a logical fallacy (i.e. simply wrong!). It allows otherwise intelligent people to dismiss great swathes of contemporary truth, common sense or other wisdom by use of the sweeping egotistical statement *"I don't believe it"*. This springs from childhood competition and conditioning and the beliefs that *"I'm right and you're wrong"*, *"I'm better than you are"* as opposed to the more mature stance of *"I'm right and so are you"* or even *"I am reviewing the situation, and may have to admit that there is truth in what you say"*. As was once said *"Be transformed by the renewing of your mind"*[2]. Actually, in life, Every Day's a School Day. (EDASD)

2. Insecure Ego

From childhood on, like puppies and kittens, we are domesticated into conforming to society's, our parents', teachers' and others' expectations. Our ego is insecure and always seeks validity from other people. It will happily trade away its power and independence (money, time, and so on…) as it wants to be made to feel important. As a result *we often give up our 'power'*.

Alternatively - and worse - our Ego tries to steal power from other people. We engage in competitive energy theft, taking part *of* the flow of life; trying to stand on other people's shoulders and toes rather than taking part *in* the flow of life on an equal and fair basis. So, if we don't give up our power, we may try to steal some from someone else to make us feel better. (See: Games People Play[3]).

3. Mind-Body Split

In Eastern thinking, in India and China, mind body and spirit are seen as interconnected, with man standing as a bridge between heaven and earth. This point of view started to disappear in Western civilization around the time of the Greek philosophers. As Renaissance scientists became interested in the body, they asked the establishment, the Medieval Catholic Church, for permission to dissect the body. Permission was given - on condition they did not touch the soul. So for several centuries medical science has investigated the hardware of the body right down to molecular and electron microscope level - but not looked at the software of the 'being'. 'Psychology' is a comparatively young science, and much of it has been concerned with the mechanics of mind, rather than applied to an understanding of the soul.

The whole of western biomedicine is based on ignoring the wholeness of the mind-body-spirit philosophy of older wisdoms. As healing is restoring harmony to the whole, Western medical philosophy is tragically doomed to fail some of the needs of our patients, due a system problem, despite the best efforts of healing practitioners. Software Being (soul) is philosophically ignored at the expense of concentrating upon Hardware Body.[4]

4. Intuition Squashed

Life is lived forwards but evaluated in retrospect. As we move forwards in life, we make a series of choices. As Professor Dumbledore said to Harry Potter:

"It is our choices, Harry, that show what we truly are, far more than our abilities."[5]

Our choices are influenced by our experience and wisdom and are made through the brain. Our brain has a left side, the seat of logic and analysis, and a right - from where intuition and creativity work. So it might be useful to learn how to make wise choices. Yet at school we learn many facts but little about how to make good choices. Learning too many facts keeps us in our left brain.

As a Professor of medical ethics said recently, "Andrew, logic can only inform - it is intuition that must always guide us. Logic unguided can lead us most elegantly up a blind alley." (I had wondered why I was meeting him in an Out of Hours consultation. This was my learning from the meeting!)

From childhood onwards, our intuition (our In-Tune Station) is squashed by those who love us, those who teach us, and others who all wish us to think as they wish us to So, we learn to ignore it (at our peril!) A good practitioner is one who knows the rules and protocols, yet can also listen to his/her intuition when it is needed to help make a courageous, rather than a by the book, decision, if the situation demands this ability.

There may be a very good reason for this culturally: a society that uses the written word to, a large extent, develops left brain skills of analysis and precision at the expense of narrative, image, emotional tone and content and creativity[6]

5. The Interconnectedness of All Things

Relativity and Quantum Mechanics tells us that at a vibrational level, everything is connected. Yet we act as if this is not true, as if we are all separate. Furthermore, Chaos Theory tells us that the beat of a butterfly's wing in Chicago can cause a hurricane in distant Honolulu. (Personally, I can't really believe this - it must be a spelling mistake. It should read "the break of a butterfly's wind" - that's rather more credible!)

So we treat each other and everything else as separate. It's very easy to dislike or hurt someone you see as separate but more difficult to choose to hurt a part of yourself.

Are we a-lone or are we all-one? If we see each other as separate, we see disease as something to be conquered, cut out, burnt or poisoned, forgetting that it is also vital to augment the body's self-healing abilities. The body's design default is the ability to heal itself, whether a cut or bruise, a fracture or an infection, yet the wonders of modern science sometimes forget this.

The narrative of medicine is Chemistry based for pathology, anatomy, physiology and much of therapeutics; though for diagnostics Physics is also used. However, in the world of IT, everyone accepts that principles of Physics are important. Once Medicine accepts these and assimilates them for pathology and therapeutics, we may indeed see quantum leaps in understanding for instance, the fact that the body is not just electric, but electronic as well, and the role in information in bodily health, and body posture and acupressure as modulating those flows; perhaps also the role of information in therapeutic substances.[7]

6. What's our Point of View in Life? – the Paradox of Life!

Are we all individuals living life or is 'life' living through us? Are we all, in fact, actors on a stage in a drama perhaps of our own making, living life and seeing it from different points of view? Is it Life itself that lives through all of us, so that it can see the overall balanced view and thus gain wisdom?

The view from the Ego is essentially through human lenses, and thus unconsciously personifies many situations and circumstances. Two hours into a long conversation, I asked my friend Stash *"Do you believe in God?"*. *"God!"* he exclaimed - *"Of course not, I believe in Life, Life with a capital L - it's here, it's now, it's everywhere, and I'm part of it!"*. One analysis of his reply could be:

1. Man who is deeply spiritual and aware of it - true.
2. Man who professes a specific religion - not true.
3. Man who is aware of the pitfall of personification as applied to the creative force of the Universe - entirely true!

Others are able to articulate a view from personal experience:

"It was clear to me that this body functions like a portal through which the energy that I am can be beamed into a three-dimensional space".[8]

Jill Bolte Taylor, Neuroanatomist whose stroke at age 37 affecting her left-brain function gave her unique insights into the left brain right brain split and the purpose of the brain.

If life is living through us, then perhaps our bodies are vehicles for an individuated part of a greater consciousness? Jean Elmiger[9] states that "life is nothing but the unfolding of vital energy", whilst others would add that this process of manifestation into physical reality happens by means of thought.[10]

Conclusion

These six system problems are rooted deeply in our thinking, not just in biomedicine, but throughout society's thinking. If you come up against any one of them, people will argue most passionately, thinking they are arguing with reason. However, they are not; they are arguing from fear. The fear that we all feel when a tightly held, highly cherished emotional belief is challenged!

I remember a friend, a very good GP, who years ago said to me *"If you showed me a hundred studies that all showed that Homeopathy worked - I still wouldn't believe them!"* System problems one, two, three, four five and six all present. (It is of course irrelevant as to whether homeopathy works or not - the same argument is used time and again in many areas, simply because people fail to understand a mechanism - or have other often unconscious, vested interests). After all: FEAR = False Evidence Appearing Real.

Fear stops us thinking laterally, fear acts to hold us within prison walls, including those of our own making and our own thinking. So what is the antidote? Support and understanding is the antidote to fear; support and understanding brings security and reassurance; support and understanding puts us in a place where we can learn. **Fear is the Lock** but **Love (Support) is the Key.**

So, the challenge for us all is to get beyond the sick (sorry, six) system problems and education is the key; education, education and education. The Latin word e-ducare means to lead out (from ignorance).

How many of the system problems apply to each of us today?

A quick guide to overcoming system problems:

a. Think for Yourself
b. Release feelings of Fear and Want
c. Acknowledge that Mind, Body and Spirit are one
d. Listen to Your Intuition, be Guided by it
e. Know that All is connected, everything is one
f. See the Whole Picture

Good luck! As they say: not a problem, just a project!

As the Chinese proverb says:

"Man who sees sky from bottom of well does not see whole picture".

Reflection points:

- Do these six system problems ring true?
- Have you ever met any of them in your professional field?
- If you have identified one (or more) can you think of any ways of understanding the issue from a bigger perspective?

Dr Patricia Saintey, Lyn Page and Andrew Tresidder

At this point let us revisit some basic mammalian physiology - after all, our bodies are mammals and have an Autonomic Nervous operating system.

The HeartMath[1] Institute's definition of resilience is:

- Your resilience capacity can be thought of as the amount of energy you can store in your inner battery.
- The greater your resilience, the more energy you'll have available when you need it.
- Having more energy means you have greater capacity to self-regulate and be in charge of how you respond in situations.
- Learning and applying energy-management skills can increase your energy reserves, thereby increasing your resilience capacity.
- Getting enough sleep and plugging energy 'leaks' so you don't waste energy is key in building and maintaining your resilience.

Stress - a corrosive factor

Stress is "a condition or feeling experienced when a person perceives that demands exceed the personal and social resources the individual is able to mobilize" [2].There can be:

- Physical stressors
- Emotional stressors
- Lack of control can be very stressful

Stress: 'demands' exceed 'resources'.

When people feel in control of a situation; when they have the training, the time and the resources to manage it, they do not feel negative stress. They may in fact feel positively stimulated (eustress). But when they feel out of control, or overwhelmed they can feel distress. When they are unable to cope with the demands placed upon them they then feel stressed; a negative feeling.

So the feeling of stress that we can have depends on how we view the situation, or the threat that confronts us. If we see it as a positive challenge, then we do not feel stressed. If we see it as overwhelming and feel out of control, then we can feel stressed. A threat to one person is an opportunity to another.

So, a lot can depend on which lenses we are looking through - the lens of experience and confidence, backed up by the right training and resources, or the lens of inadequacy, coloured by previous negative experiences.

Let's just look at the Yerkes-Dodson Curve: the Physiology of Stress, and mammals.

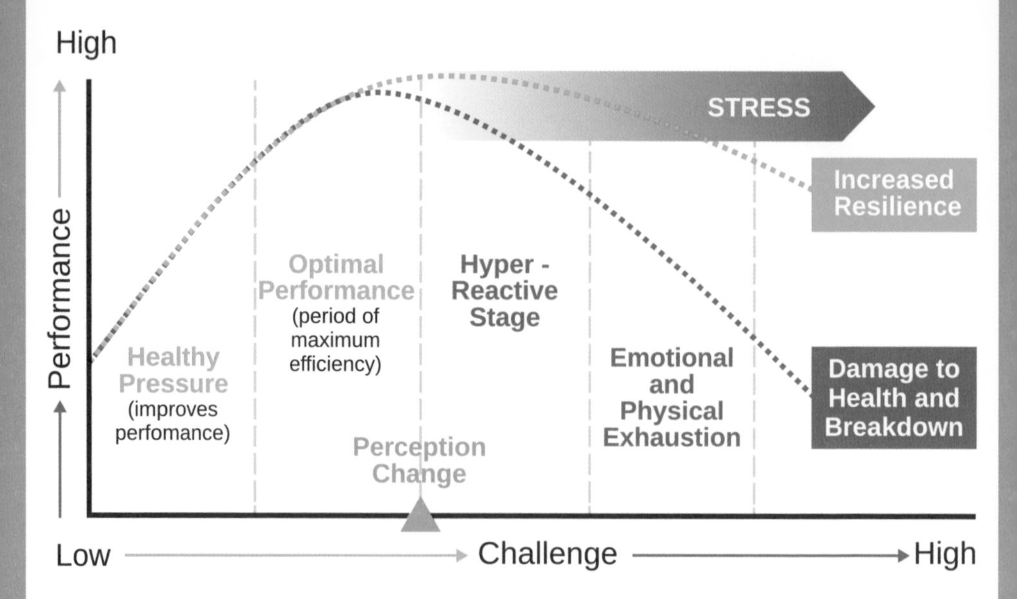

09.1 The Yerkes-Dodson Performance–Stress Curve

The diagram shows that:

- At low stimulation levels, performance is low,
- With increasing stimulation, performance increases, but…
- Beyond a certain point, further pressure results in a tail off of performance.

It is said that many managers are working to the right of the apex of the curve, at high arousal and on the downward slope. That is to say, in danger of burnout, depression, anxiety, hypertension or other physical illness.

A recent discussion with junior doctors identified that many felt that they had been to the right of the apex in certain jobs, whilst several senior doctors said that they had been somewhere on the right hand downward slope for quite a while. This is worrying…

Ideally, we should all work at between 60 and 80% of our maximum – on the upward slope. At this point we are stimulated, interested, alert, and perform well. We also the ability to work harder for a short while (increase output) when needed, and then return to a comfortable level of effortless achievement.

It is worth knowing where you are on the curve and doing an occasional rain-check! Unfortunately, the workplace often places high pressure and stimulation on employees, giving a high level of arousal, but also a tail off in performance.

W Edwards Deming's advice transformed post war Japanese industry. He wrote about statistical variance. Now I can't explain to you what that is, but his conclusion was startling:

"It is management's job to design the workplace so that the workforce can achieve effortless success - not to drive the workforce harder by exhortation or criticism." [3]

Now, a profession that dislikes being managed from the outside (such as the medical profession) has a duty. The duty is to make sure its outer structure of workplace and inner drivers of conscience and principles ensure success, otherwise we doctors can allow ourselves to burn out through our own or our patients expectations... And the most difficult biases are the ones we don't see. (See Six System Problems).

How many of us are on the downward slope on the right hand side?

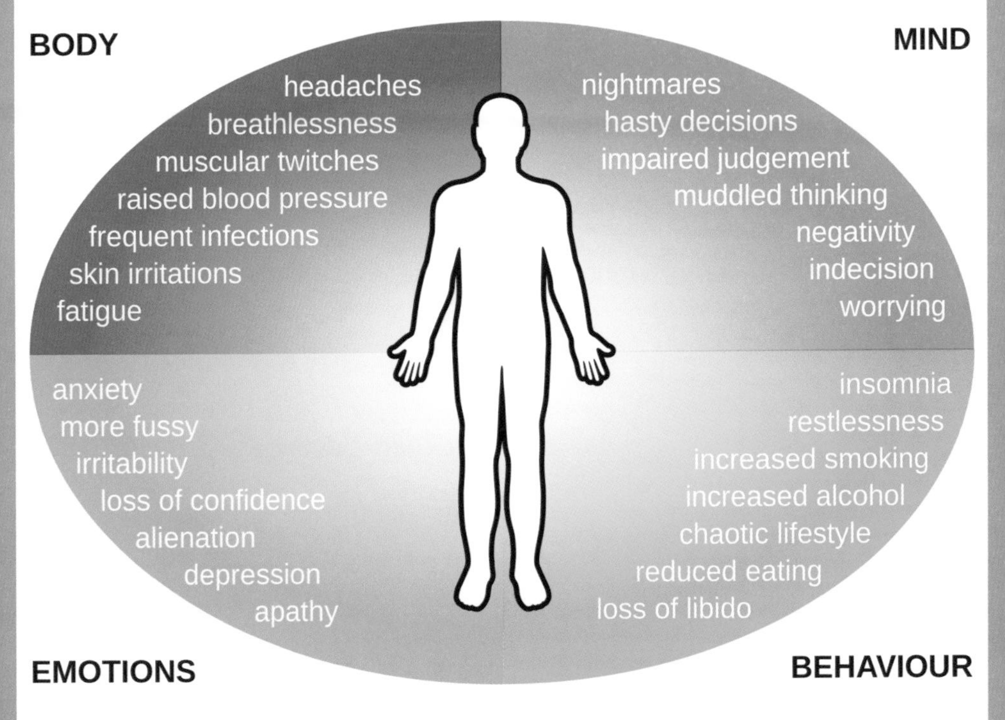

09.2 The effects of stress on the body

To look at stress and its effects fully, we'll have to look back at something we learnt a long time ago - some basic mammalian physiology.

Autonomic Nervous System

The body has both a Central and an Autonomic Nervous system. The ANS is the background computer that monitors and adjusts body function. Much of our body is controlled by the autonomic nervous system including our:

- Heart
- Brain
- Nervous system
- Vital organs

All activity is automatic and doesn't require us to think about doing it. A lot of our brain activity occurs non-consciously. Habits are pre-programmed. To change an established habit we need to interrupt our normal pattern, think about what we would like to do differently and then build a new habit to overlay over the old habit within our brain. A positive thought held for at least 20 seconds creates new neural connections.

The ANS consists of the:

- Sympathetic (Fight or Flight) nervous system
- Parasympathetic (Rest and Digest) system

There is a dynamic tension between the two at all times. When the sympathetic system is activated, the body is prepared for immediate action such as Fight or Flight. Adrenaline, noradrenaline and other stress neurotransmitters are released into the bloodstream, with the following results:

- Raised blood pressure and pulse, stronger heart beat.
- Blood is diverted away from the skin, gut and other organs (including the immune system), and channelled to the heart and muscles. Blood supply is maintained to the brain.
- Hands get sweaty, mouth gets dry.
- Breathing becomes rapid, shallow and chaotic.
- The body is alert and wide awake, and intensely aware. Sleep is unlikely.
- Vision becomes focused on central targets, peripheral vision is less important.
- The body is ready for action, for physical fight or flight (to fight a threat, or run away).

Sympathetic Drive is adapted for rapid effective 'doing' action.

At all other times, the body is on parasympathetic tone (Rest and Digest, Repair and Maintenance):

- Blood goes to gut and organs including skin.
- Blood is diverted away from the muscles.
- Hands are dry; mouth and gut secrete saliva and digestive juices.
- Breathing is slow, rhythmic and regular.

- Alertness is relaxed rather than focused. Sleep may happen.
- Vision is aware of the periphery as well as central.
- Bodily functions include effective digestion, tissue maintenance and repair.
- Healing is facilitated.

Parasympathetic drive supports 'being' and inner stillness.

If we consider other mammals in nature: cows or sheep in the field, cats on their favourite chair, etc. we find that they are all on parasympathetic drive for the vast majority of the time. (Parasympathetic Shock is a specific circumstance when facing imminent danger of death and unable to run away. The body goes into 'freeze, about to die' mode and the body is flooded by opiates. Animals recovering from this shake and shiver – a release of the Parasympathetic Shock. Humans may just bury the experience). For more on shock and Psycho Neuro Immunology there is a useful introduction by Dr Patricia Worby[4].

Fight & flight

Fight & Flight is our default response which can be very useful to us. It got us out of danger. We are running on a very old operating system which gets triggered by modern life in exactly the same way as life and death situations trigger it.

Today we have different pressures such as:
- Emails
- Smart phones
- Social media

Multi-tasking drains our energy, doesn't allow us to switch off and rest and repair. We also really struggle to concentrate on more than one or two things at a time.

We do have choices as to which cocktail of neurochemicals we wish to have running around our bodies: corrosive stress hormones, or supportive repair ones. Many humans, however, in their busy lives, especially medical and health care staff or employees driven by targets, are often on sympathetic drive from the time they wake until the time that they fall asleep exhausted. In this situation, our state of health is being dictated by adrenaline and cortisol.

Is this mammal on the 'fight and flight' setting or on the 'rest and digest' one?

The Autonomic Nervous System

We need a balance between the two elements of our autonomic nervous system (ANS):

- The parasympathetic (PNS) (rest & repair)
- The sympathetic system (SNS) (fight & flight)

We need to be able to switch between the two, however often our SNS is dominant. Not giving ourselves the opportunity to rest and repair reduces our resilience by draining our energy.

Heart Rate: the Difference Between Chaos and Coherence

Chaotic beat to beat variability (top diagram) is bad for us; 'good' coherent heart rate variability (bottom diagram) is good for us.

09.3

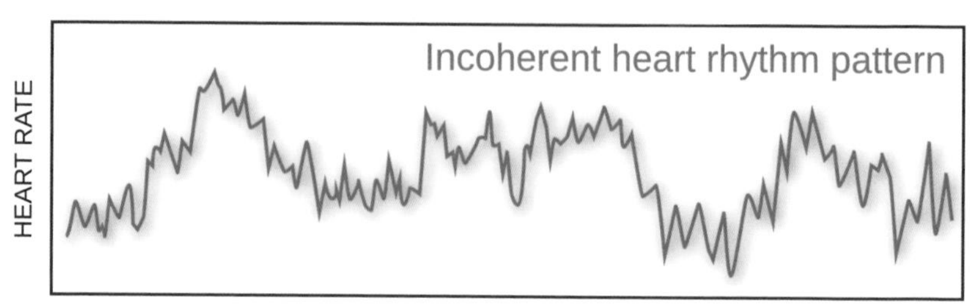

Stressful 'negative' attitudes and emotions, like frustration, anxiety and stress cause chaotic heart rhythms, leading to increased cortisol level and disruptive sleep rhythm.

09.4

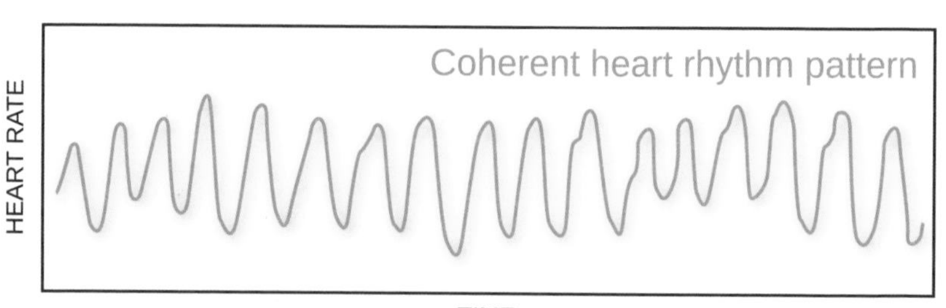

'Positive' attitudes and emotions, like wonder, appreciation, gratitude, love and compassion, create smooth, coherent heart rhythms, leading to more restful revitalising sleep.

Chaos is jumpy, jangly and irritated. Chaos is exhausting to our hearts and the rest of our body due to the multiple reactions going on:

- Releasing hormones such as adrenaline and cortisol - in preparation to run!
- Our energy levels are depleted by all this preparation and panic activity.

- We lose the ability to think clearly because part of our brain disconnects.
- We divert glucose from our brain to our muscles so we can run fast.
- Our sleep is affected adversely.

Coherence is much calmer. It is like a well-oiled machine - smooth and even. When we are coherent we:

- Release a hormone called DHEA, which is the opposite end of the spectrum to cortisol.
- Don't waste energy.
- Can think clearly as the prefrontal cortex element of our brain doesn't disconnect.
- Sleep better.

The Chemistry of Resilience

09.4

High cortisol is associated with:

- Obesity - cortisol increases fat on the waist
- Diabetes - cortisol increase blood sugar
- High blood pressure - cortisol disrupts fluid balance
- Heart disease - cortisol is implicated
- Cancer - cortisol impairs immune function
- Depression - cortisol promotes negative feelings
- Senile dementia - cortisol impairs brain function

- A 'hit' of cortisol stays in our system for longer than a 'hit' of DHEA.
- DHEA is associated with dopamine, oxytocin, and testosterone - 'feel good' hormones.
- DHEA synthetic is a banned substance in Olympic sports.
- Cortisol is useful in a spike to get us up in the morning or as fuel for exercise.
- Cortisol is not good for us if it is not 'burnt off' or used up; leaving it just sitting in our body causes problems as mentioned above.
- Our body can't differentiate between us re-telling an incident and the actual event itself so it releases more cortisol each time we recall or retell the story.

- Increasing DHEA and reducing Cortisol is something we can do for ourselves by getting ourselves into a coherent state.

We can activate our pause button and start the process of working towards a coherent state (restore balance and order) by breathing.

Emotions are the continuous dialogue occurring in our ANS at any one time. This dialogue is going on between our heart, brain, nervous system, hormonal system, vital and sensory organs. This often presents itself as 'butterflies' or stomach cramps.

A shift in emotion releases a cascade of 1,400 biochemicals that surges around our body.

Heart Focussed Breathing Promotes Coherence and Harmony

- Focus on your breathing. Make a deposit in the 'bank of inner calm'.
- Feel your tummy move away from your spine as you breathe in and back towards it as you breathe out.
- Try and breathe in a rhythm of 5 seconds in and 5 seconds out but not at the expense of comfortable, smooth and rhythmic breathing.
- Let the in breath flow smoothly followed by a smooth out breath.
- Try and maintain an easy rhythm.
- Keep your breathing fluid and light.
- It is the flow and rhythm that is most important.
- Focus on your heart and try to 'breathe through your heart' or at least your chest area.
- Don't think too hard about your breathing just try and let it be, and enjoy it.

Practice regularly throughout your day at small intervals to:

- Build a new habit.
- Increase your awareness of self.
- Give your body a chance to rest and repair.
- Plug any energy drains and even boost rather than deplete your energy levels (reverse the annual average ageing in energy terms of 3%).
- Increase DHEA in your system.
- Reduce cortisol in your system.

We can't always influence what happens to, or around us, but we can manage our reaction to events. One (wo)man's stress is another (wo)man's growth opportunity.

"Between stimulus and response there is a space. In that space is our power to choose our response. In our response lies our growth and our freedom."

Viktor Frankl

General Adaptation Syndrome - Hans Selye

Canadian-Hungarian endocrinologist Prof Hans Selye studied stress and illness. He noted that in infectious illnesses, patients had similar responses whatever the infectious agent. Further observation showed a common sequence of three responses when animals were injected with toxic substances:

1. The adrenal glands swelled (the adrenals, we remember, are where the stress response hormones of adrenaline, noradrenaline and corticosteroids are made).
2. Lymph nodes and other organs that produced white blood cells (infection fighting areas) first swelled, then got smaller.
3. Finally the stomach and intestines developed ulcers and bled (the stress response to surgery of an acute gastric ulcer is well recognised).

From these observations he derived his General Adaptation Syndrome, and postulated that whatever the noxious stimulus, the body would react to the stress with a series of specific responses. He looked at rats, monkeys and humans and realized that physical or emotional stress started and maintained patterns of imbalance that led to illness, disease and eventually death.

09.5

General Adaption Syndrome (Selye 1936)

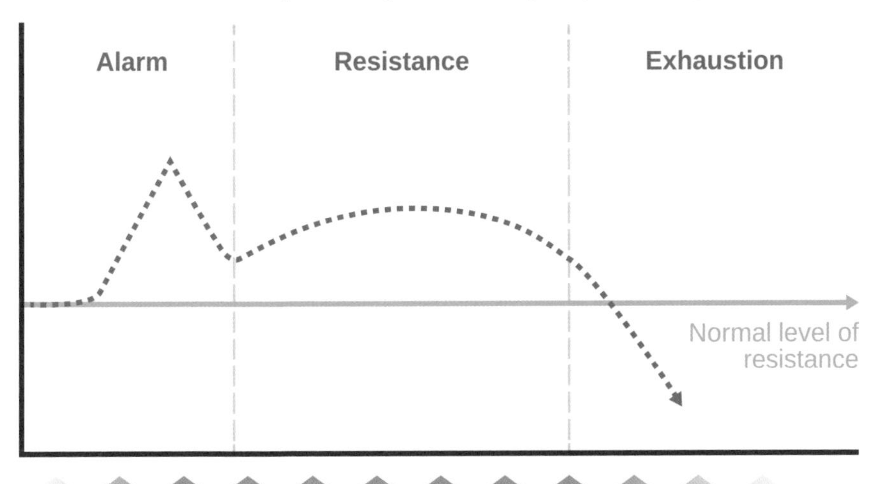

In the 'alarm' phase, a shock, surprise or threat activates the sympathetic nervous system and a fight or flight response happens. We are ready for action. The digestion and the immune system is put on hold while we deal with the threat. The adrenal glands pour out stress neurotransmitters. If the threat then goes away, we relax and recover, and the adrenal glands go back to normal.

In the 'resistance' phase, the stimulus or threat continues. The body tries to maintain homeostasis. We initially resist the threat then become externally adapted to it. On the inside, our adrenal glands hypertrophy in order to deliver high levels of stress chemicals on a long term basis. Blood pressure may rise, the immune system is compromised, and we may start to develop illness within.

In the final Phase - exhaustion - the body can no longer cope with the continued stimulus or threat. The adrenal glands atrophy, and the long-term effects of postponing rest and digest, repair and maintenance become obvious. Chronic degenerative illness sets in, vitality decreases, and we find ourselves on the slippery downward slope towards final illness and death.

In his experiments on rats, Selye kept two groups. The controls scampered about happily in their cages and lived a long time. The study group were chilled to 4°C. Initially they had an alarm phase of hyperactivity, then resistance set in and they looked normal on the outside. However, after initial hypertrophy, the adrenal glands became exhausted, and the rats died early.

Interestingly, if you remove the stimulus from adapted rats (or people), they actually go through the symptoms and signs of the alarm phase again. This can be painful, so sometimes we avoid this by keeping adapted to the stimulus. This may explain part of the physical phenomenon of withdrawal from substance addiction. We don't want to have the alarm phase again (in which our bodies adapt back to normality).

A classic example would be the person drinking ten cups of coffee a day who complains of headaches. The likely cause of the headaches is the coffee drinking but when it is cut out, there is often a severe withdrawal headache. In the same way, give a busy (wo)man a half-day off, and (s)he'll probably fill it with another activity, rather than find a way of relaxing.

So, going cold turkey from your coffee or other regular habits is something that people often avoid. Often people swap one addiction for another.

The big problem is, in our human lives, we perceive many things as stressful stimuli, from emotional threats, to loud noises, to chemical challenges from food, air and water, to excess cold or heat, demands of work and so on. Many of us are on chronic sympathetic overdrive, without realizing it.

Some people are addicted to work, some to smoking, some to alcohol, some to excitement, some to soft and hard drugs (if there is a difference). Therefore, one wonders if a very common addiction amongst the medical profession (among others) is to our own body's production of adrenaline. This addiction actually feels quite good (we feel stimulated and buzzing) but is corrosive to our own inner healing and relationships, let alone to our personal health in the long term. In essence, it may be addiction to one's own adrenaline! (Adrenalism)

The Bucket of Stresses

Just looking at the stresses we have in life, we can only cope with so much. It's a bit like a bucket - you can tip this in, then that, then this, then some more - and then it overflows…

© pixelpup, istock photos

What are the stresses? Any demands placed upon the body:

- Poor diet, poor posture, poor sleep, dehydration
- Foods (sugar, coffee, others)
- Alchohol and drug taking (intoxicants)
- Excess work demands, unhappiness, emotional load
- Relationship issues, poor emotional coping skills strategies
- Financial pressure, trauma, physical or emotional
- Chemicals in the atmosphere, food, environment (remember aspartame, the sweetener, breaks down at body temperature to phenylalanine and methanol, metabolised to formaldehyde, a neurotoxin and class 1 carcinogen)
- Medication, herbicides and pesticides
- Electromagnetic fields
- Lack of sunlight, lack of fresh air, lack of exposure to nature
- Bonfire smoke, (including cigarette smoke), moulds, fungi

Our bodies can only respond in certain ways - fever, rashes, tingling, numbness, nausea, vomiting, diarrhoea, runny nose, cough, headache, low mood, fatigue, poor sleep, heartburn, irritability and so on - so whatever the stimulus, if it's too much, we may end up with one or more of these responses.

That's why a farming friend would always cut out milk and cream at the pollen season. His otherwise dreadful hay fever was ok if he removed the stimulus of the other foreign proteins (cow's milk) when the grass pollen was around. The bucket wasn't overflowing into symptoms - it could cope with just the pollen, or the dairy products but not both together. For an interesting discussion of food intolerance and adaptation, see the work of Richard Mackarness.[5]

So it's worth being aware of all these factors, and trying to achieve a balance, especially when ill... Remember the 'lost art of convalescence'.

Love Your Immune System! (LYIS)

If you have a bacterial infection, do antibiotics make you better? No, antibiotics only kill bacteria! It's always the immune system that makes us better - the immune system consists of white blood cells, lymph glands, the spleen and other groups of tissues. These produce responses to foreign invaders such as bacteria or viruses, or other foreign proteins.

So what can we do to support it our immune system? We can love it:

- Good quality sleep refreshes and supports the immune system; rest can be vital.
- The Breath! - regular rhythmic breathing from the diaphragm brings coherence into the system. (irregular shallow upper chest breathing engenders chaos in the system). Make a deposit in the 'bank of inner calm'.
- High quality fresh food.
- Plenty of fresh water and minimizing tea, coffee and alcohol.
- Kindness and gratitude activate the system.
- Avoid stress and electronic devices when trying to rest - you can't do both at the same time.
- Laughter, joy, dance, happiness and zest for life activate positive neurochemicals.
- Exercise (when not acutely ill) supports our wellbeing.
- Sunlight and vitamin D production by day are valuable, or supplementation in low sunshine months.
- Supplementing with appropriate vitamins and minerals can be vital (the immune system needs plenty of vitamin C and Zinc, and many people are already compromised. Most people are deficient in magnesium).
- Appropriate support with Echinacea or other herbs may be useful short term during illness (one study showed Echinacea more effective than Tamiflu at reducing symptoms and speeding recovery in influenza).[6]

Other important factors are:

- Reducing the load of moulds, spores, fungi etc. by ventilating the living space.
- Reducing Electromagnetic stress (expect to hear more about this - remember how 'safe' asbestos was for many years). Electromagnetic pollution from RF (Microwave) transmissions, 'dirty electricity' and EM fields.[7]
- Reduce the chemical load: Foreign chemicals, insecticides, etc. Also colourings and sweeteners (at body temperature aspartame breakdown products include methanol).
- Avoid devitalised food, low vitamin and mineral content.
- Avoid refined carbohydrates in excess.
- Honour your body's need to work with circadian rhythms of light and dark.
- Love your body - how can you expect it to work well for you if you don't love it (much, or at all).

Above all, learn the ways of health and be kind to yourself.

Sleep

Importantly, eight hours sleep in darkness starting well before midnight ensures maximal refreshment of sleep, and optimal melatonin production. Grandmother's wise advice that the hours before midnight count double has some truth in it. Sleep is "*when our nervous system becomes quieter, our eyes are closed, muscles relaxed, and our consciousness nearly suspended*" [8]. Sleep is what all mammals need. Deprived of sleep, animals and people become ill, disorientated and can develop mental disorders. Sleep deprivation is used as a method of torture. Babies sleep for most of the day: twenty two hours in the first few days and then progressively less as they get older.

During sleep, the brain discharges redundant patterns of electrical activity, has dreams, and rehearses new neuronal programmes that lead to thought, sensations or patterns of movement. In sleep, old patterns of thought can surface (Human Givens). Good quality sleep in darkness, free from light, noise and electrical fields, gives refreshment. It enables the body to relax and repair itself, (the parasympathetic mode), and is vital for medium and long term health and well-being. The best quality sleep is in tune with Circadian Rhythms. During darkness, the pineal gland produces melatonin. Peak production is before midnight with a tailing off later. Melatonin is a key substance that helps regulate many body hormonal and neuro-endocrine systems and is also a powerful anti-oxidant. All body cells, including skin, contain cryptochromes, which respond to light and other electromagnetic fields. If darkness is interrupted by light falling on the body during sleep, then melatonin production ceases for the rest of the night. This handicaps the immune system and leads to poor quality sleep.

The light intensity needed to stop melatonin production is low, and varies with the wavelength. So we can actually tolerate a slightly higher intensity of red light than of whiter before melatonin production is compromised. Blue light before sleep (computer screen, reading devices etc.) will postpone the onset of melatonin production for up to two hours because the body thinks it's bright sunshine. It appears that electromagnetic fields may also disrupt sleep. This is of importance because many people have electrical appliances in their bedrooms, and sometimes transmitting devices in or near the house which effectively pollutes the health of the sleep environment. If this happens, restless unrefreshing sleep can result, and melatonin production may be compromised, with the result of medium and long term ill-health.

Enthusiasm and youth often tempts us to sacrifice our sleep, and electric light effectively makes our bodies think they are in summer all year round (sixteen hours of daylight a day). If you keep chickens commercially to lay eggs, in winter they lose their feathers and stop laying eggs when day length shortens. To make more profit, you keep them inside with a light on for sixteen hours a day. Then you get an egg a day per hen. But they do not live for as long. Likewise, our bodies, if made to think it is summer all year, adapt, age faster, and develop insulin resistance, weight gain and all sorts of other things we don't really need. They wear out early. Another overlooked factor is the Glutamate Surge. Alcohol acts as a depressant, so makes people drowsy. However, the body counteracts the depressant effect by producing glutamate, and the action of the glutamate continues after the depressant effect of the alcohol has worn off. Hence why some people are suddenly wide awake some four to six hours after going to sleep. Their brain is woken up by glutamate.

In Lights Out[9], TS Wiley argues that our mammalian bodies are designed to work with circadian rhythms in pattern through the seasons: to crave carbohydrate in summer when long day length results in insulin resistance and laying down of fatty stores. In winter, short day length and less availability of food means ketosis and weight loss. But in the land of electric light and supermarkets full of sweet things, winter never comes, so year on year we gain weight to satisfy our biology. The results are: obesity, heart disease, diabetes, and so on. Scary reading but it makes sense. For more information on sleep hygiene see the appendix[10]. A good routine and relaxation prior to bed can make a big difference.

For medical practitioners, the sleep quality of patients is very important. Poor sleep at a physical level may point to sleep apnoea in some cases, but in many cases, people who wake up unrefreshed have an environmental cause such as electromagnetic pollution in their living space, or possibly geopathic stress.

ElectroMagnetic Pollution and Electromagnetic Stress

(This may be ahead of time, and is written with the benefit of experiencing many cases of electrosensitivity. This is a much debated area, and will arouse considerable passion, as 'Safety ALWAYS lags behind technological advances' (Think tyre tread, seat-belts, asbestos, lead in petrol etc.) The reader is asked to research and make up their own mind…

Human health is a delicate balance. It can be adversely affected by interfering factors such as chemical pollution, smoke, pollens, moulds, the food we eat, what we drink, lack of sleep, lack of fresh air, lack of sunlight, lack of fresh water and so on. Electromagnetic pollution is another cause, which affects the body. Our bodies were developed over millions of years in an environment free from pollution and man-made EM signals (which are up to 10^{18} stronger than background signals and from a router or cordless phone up to 6V/m and 10,000µW/m^2), whilst the body uses minute micro-currents for cellular function.

Symptoms may be none or include tiredness, poor quality sleep, irritability, heart palpitations, headaches and a feeling of pressure in the head, speech and thinking disturbance, brain fog, dizziness, tinnitus, vertigo, tingling and odd sensations in the limbs, joint pains, rashes, nosebleeds and others. It is not known why some people react to these and others do not, however it may be that heterogeneity of genetic make-up, nutritional status, and other factors predispose people to develop the condition once sensitised. Certainly general factors like lack of sleep can exacerbate the issue.

An unfortunate myth/mantra perpetuated in science and by private industry bodies is that non-thermal = non-harmful [now known to be FALSE] (i.e. if it doesn't heat you over six minutes). Moreover, this completely ignores all signal effects, which have known biological consequences. If ants can die from proximity to a wifi router, mobile phone or laptop on wifi (because they lose their ability to navigate, as caused by a signal, not a thermal effect)[11], rats' retinas be harmed by certain frequencies of LED light[12] whilst our ears can detect a billionth of a watt and our eyes a single photon, then is it surprising that measurable EM or RF (radiofrequency, the new name for microwave) fields affect some people? Often with nervous system symptoms to extremely weak fields.

A big problem that we all face as Clinicians, Scientists and Researchers is that the Medicine we have learnt is predominantly based on the discipline of chemistry, not physics. Yes, MRI Scanners and CT scans are physics (i.e, information technology) based, however the vast majority of the narrative of pathology, physiology, anatomy, diagnostics and therapeutics is chemistry based. Yet we are seeing in the field of IT that a physics based understanding of technology has changed our world (yes, your phone, computer, internet use and so on, has chemistry based hardware, but the software working of it is largely physics based information technology). Furthermore, all clinicians are aware, from the history of medicine that new insights into understanding are always occurring.

There is a growing awareness that the human body works on biophotons and information flows[13] and electromagnetics as well as chemistry, and that proteins in cell walls work as switching transistors. No wonder that exposure to certain frequencies of EM or RF fields at low power can have a biological effect - because this is how the cells work on microvoltage and microwattage powers[14]. And of course the first noticed symptomatic effects will be on the nervous system, especially if already compromised due to (common) sub-clinical nutritional deficiencies of Omega 3 fatty acids, B Vitamins (consider pellagra, as a deficiency illness), intra-cellular magnesium, zinc, manganese and others. Toxicity from mercury, aluminium and others cause problems.

Electromagnetic problems are caused by:

1. field effects from cables and appliances (such as lights, hairdryers, washing machines, cookers, bedside radios and so on).
2. signal and power effects from microwave transmitting technology, such as microwave ovens, mobile phone masts, cordless phone base stations and handsets, mobile phones, wireless routers, Wii devices, laptop computers, printers, home and office alarm sensors, iPads and others, baby alarms, Smart Meters for utilities, and wireless central heating controls, and Bluetooth devices in the car.
3. 'Dirty electricity', implicated in health issues.[15] Transmitting technology is now widespread compared to thirty years ago. Many houses now contain a range of transmitters from the list above. Some only transmit when used (leaky microwave ovens and mobile phones) others for 24 hours a day, such as wifi routers, home alarms, cordless phones, baby and domestic alarms and others. (Microwaves were used and made people unwell during the Cold War).

Accepted biological effects of EM fields include increased incidence of childhood leukaemia[16], adverse effects on sperm production, pregnancy success, embryo development, hormonal disruption and others; whilst many diseases such as depression, Motor Neurone and Parkinson's diseases, several cancers, behavioural problems, cataracts and others have an association with EM Fields.

Mechanisms include changes in calcium efflux/influx, failure of repair of DNA breaks, blood brain barrier permeability, heat shock protein production, disruption of vital melatonin production (by blue light from screens), general sympathetic (stress) upregulation of the body and others including probably disruption of cell to cell signalling. The overall effect may be to age us all more quickly...

The Council of Europe recommends a Precautionary approach, although current UK Public Health England advice is based on heating effects of transmissions only, not the observed signal effects. IARC currently says that transmitting technologies are a Class 2b possible carcinogen. What should you do to help your health? Learn about the issue (and remember that industry pressure may stop much discussion or reporting of the issue, or ridicule the 'Canaries in the Coal Mine' who are the early sufferers). Further references can be found in the appendix.[17]

The key is to minimize your exposure in the home, especially during sleep time.

- Switch off wifi routers, boosters and cordless phone base stations and any other devices you can (wherever they are in the house - remember the signal is designed to go throughout the house). Consider getting a corded landline.
- Put iPads, phones and others onto airplane mode.
- Consider a wired router and adaptor system for the computer to use through the ring main. Remember that your wireless router and other convenience devices are Class 2B possible carcinogens (may cause cancer).
- Consider electromagnetic hygiene and ask yourself if you really need wireless gadgets on all the time. Is society addicted?
- And learn about everything you can to protect your health!

In summary

Remember our own biases - if we've not been taught about something, it's easy to ignore or dismiss it. Important factors that impact upon health, not widely taught at medical or nursing schools are:

1. Nutrition, especially at micronutrient level.
2. Health as a concept.
3. Software Being (man as an electromagnetic being).
4. Interpersonal Psychology and Games.
5. Environmental factors and pollution.

Reflection points:

- Are you on sympathetic or parasympathetic drive for most of the time?
- How is your breathing: Coherent or chaotic?
- What are your major stressors? Are they threats or opportunities?
- How does Selye's Adaptation Syndrome help to explain things that happen in your life, or that of people you know?
- What habits will you change?
- How is your sleep?
- Do you switch all your devices off at night to ensure high quality sleep?
- What do you understand by electromagnetic hygiene?
- What does HALT stand for? (Hungry, Angry, Late and Tired - four drivers of poor performance that can be addressed)

A short resume to highlight a curriculum gap and to stimulate avenues of enquiry!

Our bodies were developed over millions of years to eat roots, shoots, nuts, fruit, vegetables, raw meat and to drink water. Now, we're not suggesting that you should kill your own meat, or find rainwater to drink; however, the fuel we eat and drink now is often far removed from the design default. Alongside this intake, our very own microbiome of gut flora developed to coexist with us in symbiotic relationship, nurtured by this diet. Eating a healthy diet, full of high vitality foods, results in high vitality for us.

Grains appeared in the diet ten thousand years ago. The composition of modern wheat has changed substantially even over the last century and is now often contaminated by herbicides or pesticides. Dr Sarah Myhill[1], notes that we hominids have had 200,000 years of a hunter-gatherer diet, 10,000 years of a glucogenic, and a hundred and fifty years of a glucotoxic diet.

Our ancestors ate fresh food in season. Intake of animal, fish or vegetable fat (not hydrogenated, of course) would be burnt to ketone bodies and metabolized to water and CO_2. In late summer, with long day lengths and fruit in plenty, we would gorge ourselves on available carbohydrate, any of which not immediately burnt would be converted to fat to store ready for winter and food shortages. When we burnt off fat stores in times of food shortage, we would be in ketosis for months at a time. (NB ketosis is not the same as ketoacidosis).

Civilisation learnt to preserve food to overcome times of scarcity; overconsumption all year round did not exist. Drying, fermenting (think sauerkraut), smoking and salting were some older methods used, otherwise fresh food rots. Bottling, canning and freezing have been used for over a century, whilst irradiation is much more recent. Cooking has been used with heat for millennia; however cooking with microwaves is very recent. Recent technology may not mean healthy (you can leave an irradiated tomato or apple on the window sill for several weeks without it going mouldy - so you have to wonder if there is as much vitality, life force and goodness in them as in the fresh variety).

Traditional processing aimed to provide enough to avoid starvation in winter and spring. In the past, many people only had access to local fruit and vegetables and changed tastes according to availability and season. Now, food industry production includes many good and worthy producers, local and national. Modern trade and processing provide a wide range of food choices all year round to many, with a distribution system that brings many benefits to us. However, maximizing profit in the short term (a legal obligation for public companies) involves extending shelf life and often 'adding value'. Many added value processed foods use inexpensive initial ingredients: sugar, carbohydrates, and high fructose corn syrup are often used as cheap fillers. The main problem for our bodies is that many of us indulge in over-consumption. Overeating stresses the organism. The need for long shelf life led to the development of margarine and hydrogenated fats (always including trans fatty acids - now known to be unhealthy).

Dietary fashions come and go, and we have seen a 200 year pendulum swing of sugar usage, compounded by a 50 year fashion of 'low fat'. (Experts were hired by a particular industry to divert attention from one class of foods - so they chose to demonise fats. In this time, diabetes rates have soared, (especially in countries with high consumption of sweetened drinks). We can easily crave sweet things (perhaps because breast milk is sweet), and can get a quick 'sugar high', which, if life is miserable, can help the day seem more pleasant. The sugar / carbohydrate consumption is also addictive. The result is often obesity, even in childhood (many parents say "he/she'll only drink juice or squash, not water" - a triumph for the marketing industry!). If the aim of the food industry, mandated by government, were to ensure the integrity of our health, as well as to make profits, then we would see different approaches.

Currently our diets are often short in essential ingredients, including omega 3 fatty acids, magnesium, zinc, B vitamins and others. This can result in decreased vitality, low mood and physical symptoms. At the population level, selenium deficiency leads to increased rates of cancer. Yet the whole area of nutrition is a curriculum gap for nearly all health professionals.

Fermented foods such as sauerkraut seem to support a healthy shift in our microbiome, whereas refined sugar does the opposite. Antibiotics can cause major adverse changes in the microbiome.

Lessons from some of the longest living healthy populations in the world suggest we should under consume not over consume, should eat mainly vegetables and fruit, as well as some fat and protein, that a large amount of our food should be lightly cooked or raw and finally that we should exercise our bodies and practice happiness! Following these principles, it seems that we are often eating too much carbohydrate. Maybe there is a fashion swing under way to return towards healthy eating? There will be arguments from many, either because of what they have been taught, from personal habits, or from vested interests to sway us one way or another.

Herbs and spices have been used for health for centuries; many are important.

Perhaps the three that can help human health most are garlic, turmeric and cinnamon, with powerful anti-inflammatory effects amongst other benefits. It is now thought that an important causation of much chronic illness is inflammation in the body. Herbs can modulate this, whilst careful choice in diet (avoidance of refined carbohydrates and other 'foods') can also benefit us substantially.

Healthy eating underpins physical health - so as a society, and as professionals, we need to learn more about this. It's often worth starting from first principles. When you cook, if you can recognize where your food comes from before you prepare it, then it's likely to be healthier for you.

Expect to hear much more about nutrition for health, and functional medicine in the years ahead. Remember first principles: 95% of marketing is designed to make you unhappy with what you already have (fear-based, shame-based, envy-based) and 5% will alert you to new opportunities that are important for you personally. The challenge is in deciding which is which! canceractive.com has some helpful research-based advice on nutrition.

Body Structure

A body needs to move, have good structure, be adjusted and fine-tuned if structure goes out of balance. It works best if free from tension but it may need healing support if injured.

What can we do to help? Keeping our bodies strong with physical work and exercise; approaches such as Tai Chi, Yoga, Pilates, sports, Alexander Technique and many others can put regular deposits into the Bank of Health. When we need help with imbalances and injuries, structural adjustments and exercises from techniques such as massage, osteopathy, chiropractic, physiotherapy and others can each be valuable.

Bodies heal themselves from injuries as best they can, naturally repairing cuts, bruises and breaks. Medical expertise may be needed, however here are two tips for the home treatment of minor injuries:

1. Arnica for bruises - every sports man and woman should have it available, both as cream and in potency.
2. Lavender Oil for minor burns - great to put neat onto the skin for an oven burn - should be kept in every kitchen!

Possible fruitful lines of future enquiry:

- The microbiome
- Functional Medicine
- Eating mindfully
- Harms from glyphosate and other chemicals
- Safety (or not) of sweeteners
- Micronutrient content
- Vitality of food
- Herbs for health

As health professionals, we make relationships with our patients, our colleagues, our administrative staff, management, and others. All of these are important and some of them will last a long time, so it's worth taking care to nurture and garden these relationships, especially with other hospital colleagues. By paying attention to relationships, not only do we feel better, and perform better, but we see and find the best in others.

It is in our relationships that we learn and grow; sometimes those who give us a hard time are the ones who love us the most, on another level…

Focus on the positives. Remember: everyone is guided by best intention. Life is about growing, learning wisdom, and maturity. It is always worth trying to see the other person's point of view, rather than just get entrenched in our own.

Relationships

Relationships give us the opportunity:

- to learn and grow
- to learn about ourselves
- to learn about others

Relationships may have a beginning, middle and end, timewise. A relationship consists of two or more people (or animals, plants or objects) and the bond between them. The bond is a connection, association or involvement. Connections start with an Energy Flow of Attention.

The connection may have an emotional component, in which case it becomes an attachment. Moreover, because humans are emotional beings, it often does. Attachment = Connection + Feeling.

The forming and release of attachments is what happens when relationships begin and end. Attachments can be charged with positive or negative feelings (e.g. like or dislike). The feelings represent judgments that we make, and reflect our own internal emotional needs and weather.

Attachments have a purpose; they reflect our inner needs and help them get fulfilled. The inner need includes the feeling of 'security'.

Security

A baby needs a mother and becomes attached to a significant adult - usually to its own mother, or failing that, another human being. The baby grows into a small child, who develops other attachments, and may release former ones. A baby duckling needs a mother and becomes attached to a mother duck (or, as is well known, to a person or even a dog if that's who its 'significant adult' is). Many small children become attached to a teddy bear, a doll, or a pet. Older children can be attached to other things like computer games, clothes, model trains, collecting things, and so on. Children form relationships in their peer group; often boys with boys, and girls with girls. In their teens, boys and girls often become interested in the other gender as part of socialisation and maturity, or form a relationship with a friend of the same gender.

At some point, many people choose a life partner, or, over a lifetime, a series of life partners. As we mature, we make and release attachments to learn, to fulfil our needs, and to grow. Attachments can also have consequences that can hold us back: the six-year-old inside the grown-up may still have an attachment to Mummy, to a favourite toy, device or behaviour, as can the 10-year-old, the fifteen year old and the twenty year old and so on! Let alone the Inner Toddler! Secure early attachments help us grow safely.

If an attachment is broken, the person has reactions as they transit the phases of 'loss' and 'grief', starting with shock and denial, visiting anger and guilt, bargaining, depression and finally acceptance, as the attachment is then released and the person becomes whole - older and wiser.

Relationships may follow from meetings. There are three possible lengths of the relationship: a **reason**; a **season** (or several) or a **lifetime**.

The wisdom comes from knowing which is which and whether to nurture (always) but also when to release, (with kindness). It may be worth asking yourself: what is my goal in this relationship? Is it a heart connection? Or is it better to keep a safe distance? How much are my own needs driving me?

SSSCR. Child (and Adult) Development.

Growing up is the purpose of life and of child development. Some say that children are given to us as a gift; others, that children are just lent to us for a while, as they grow up into independent adults. These principles of growth and development apply not just to the child, but to the child within each adult. That means all of us!

As a parent, all one has to do is produce a competent adult citizen around the age of 18 (give or take a few years!)

Moreover, all it takes is 3S's, a C and an R. What is needed for good emotional development is: Security; Stimulation; Support (In short, love and nurture). What the parents have to inspire is: Control (self-control), and Responsibility (That's all…! Perhaps you can fill out the details of each day and year?)

Remember, the word 'Responsibility' can be split in two: Response - Ability. That is, we each have the ability to choose our response at every moment.

Taking responsibility can lead to transformation.

As a child, the receiver of the SSSCR, we look to one or more significant adults to help us with this, and as an example – very often parents, but also teachers, relatives, and many others that we come into contact with. We develop an attachment; a secure attachment allow us to grow easily. Insecure attachments can cause all sorts of problems.

The quality of the attachment to the Primary Care Giver is key to secure emotional development (Bowlby). The security of early relationships, including parental love, helps us mature to a state of Inner Security. As a Child of the Universe, we grow into a Citizen of the World in our relationship to Life.

The Emotional Climate that we live in is also important:

- If we live in a happy household where we are valued and supported, we learn values of support and love.
- If we live in a house of arguments and criticism, we learn to criticise, to argue, and do not develop self esteem - except at someone else's expense.
- If we are ignored, we learn to hook attention, or we drift into apathy, or we learn to tread our own path in life.

So, SSSC and R produce a competent adult. Of course, it doesn't always happen quite like that. This leads on to looking at how life is lived…

The Solihull Triangle

We all need to feel safe and secure before we can develop or change - a useful model for communication is the Solihull Triangle:

1. Containment: Safety/Feeling Supported
2. Reciprocity: Conversation/Dialogue
3. Behaviour Management: Ability to achieve effective growth and change

11.1

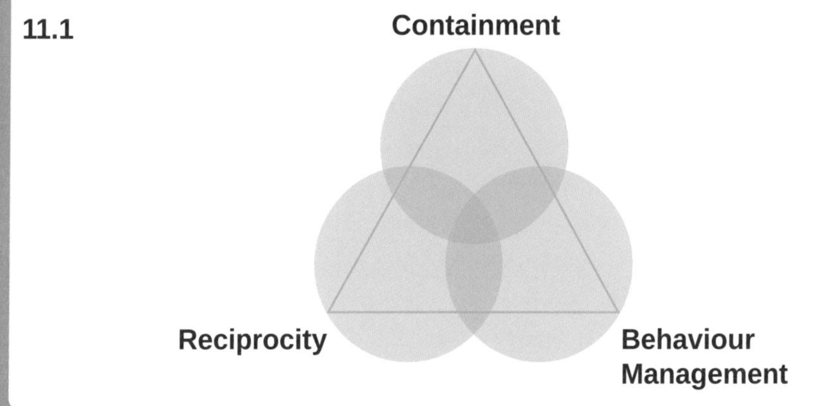

How does this work? First we have to start a relationship where the other feels safe and secure (containment). Next we can develop the relationship with a dialogue/conversation (reciprocity). Finally we have a chance of achieving change or growth (if that is what's needed).

Imagine the opposite. Pretend you are a GP, looking at the computer and a patient comes into the room, smelling of cigarettes. You say: "You must be on 20 a day, well you'll have to stop, won't you?". What do you think your chances of success of helping the patient stop smoking are? (about zero. Furthermore, the possibility of complaint is almost certain!). People may not remember what we say, but they always remember how we make them feel.

It's the long-term relationships with our colleagues where we build alliances and friendships that can be really crucial to our effectiveness and happiness. To be able to walk into a department on the first day and change things is unlikely to win immediate friends - it's more likely to build resistance. However that doesn't stop you from noticing where change may need to happen and developing a plan for this! (See Seven Habits of Highly Effective People, p159).

At some point we grow away from the security of parental love, and mature to a state of Inner Security. Though still a Child of the Universe, we become a mature citizen of the World, connected to 'life' through our own Earth Star Chakra.

For effective change, people have to feel safe. Sometimes it doesn't go smoothly. Have you ever felt upset, let down, sad, frustrated, irritated, angry or worried by someone or their actions? If so, you're in good company; we all have! But you've also been hooked into the Drama Triangle.

As a health professional, you are a leader, so make some investments. Invest in relationships with your colleagues, especially all those you work with.

Finally, remember, we can always learn from the people we meet: 'everyone is my teacher' at some level. **EIMT**. Every day's a school day… with an unwritten script… **EDASD.**

Life's Unwritten Lesson Plan

Human beings are natural learners, as they say "I just can't help learning - it's in my genes!"

Perhaps life is always offering us unconscious participation in a meaningful setting, yet the lesson plan is not always obvious at the time.

Life is full of learning opportunities, both of factual knowledge, and about life; how people tick, how we interact with others, and how we ourselves tick. Indeed, life often mirrors back to us our own issues. "You get back what you give out" or "You reap as you sow".

Yet few of us start each day realising which lesson we are about to learn about life, let alone how the lesson will evolve. However, the day always does unfold, and so do the lesson(s) offered to us. Often, to make it easy, the lesson comes in three different ways. I recall surgeries when I have seen three different presentations of a condition, or three different ways to manage a similar set of presenting problems. Then there are days when issues of tolerance, discretion, or other issues, come up multiple times.

In a wider context, in learning in life, (and at work), we are all ever learning and relearning the lessons of relating to others, and lessons such as patience, discretion, nurturing, self-nurturing, friendship, detachment and many others. The lesson plan is there, perhaps unwritten, or at least not obvious to each of us as we plough through the day. Key lessons are how we use our Power, whether we Respect others, and what Boundaries we honour.

A successful businessman once told me that he looks forward to every day as a clean sheet, an opportunity to have fun, to learn, and to make a difference.

Kolb[1] tells us that the learning cycle is: experience, reflect and learn. To adequately reflect we need time and support. Also very useful is the intention to reflect - for if we intend to reflect and we do so fully, then we gain every possible ounce of learning that we can from each situation, opportunity or consultation. Consultations, and the interaction with colleagues through the day provides multiple opportunities for learning lessons such as discretion, friendship, warmth, love, support, detachment and so on.

Perhaps every moment of life is pregnant with the possibility of rich and deep meaning?

Perhaps life offers us many opportunities for learning, all presented as unwritten lesson plans - or rather written and savoured in retrospect, or even, if we are lucky and aware, as we experience them?

Reflection points:

- What can we learn from relationships?
- What have you learnt from your early relationships?
- Have you observed anyone with insecurity which comes from early attachment problems?
- How does the Solihull triangle apply in your professional life?
- What have you learned today or recently?

12 Transitions and Life Changes In One's Lifespan

Dr Robin Philipp

"He who is of calm and happy nature will hardly feel the pressure of age, but to him who is of an opposite disposition youth and age are equally a burden".

Plato

"Anyone who stops learning is old, whether at twenty or eighty. Anyone who keeps learning stays young. The greatest thing in life is to keep your mind young."

Henry Ford

Life has a pattern and each stage has a deeper meaning. Surface disturbance can stop us seeing deeply.

Shakespeare's seven ages of men can be reframed as seven stages of a health professional's career, Starting with student motivation and career choice, Leading through the undergraduate years to house officer level, Transitioning to specialty choice, the newly-appointed consultant and Progression to senior consultant level posts, and the roles, towards later Looking towards retirement and beyond.

If we give attention to the transitions we go through by accepting the 'being' and enjoying of each stage (cf mindfulness) we enjoy a smooth and seamless flow of changes. At each stage we can remain aware at all times of our inner development and maturity in moving forwards. We acquire knowledge and experience, insight and understanding, and can then apply the accumulated wisdom for the benefit of patients, colleagues, and ourselves.

In Act II, Scene 7 of William Shakespeare's As You Like It, the jaded, cynical, and melancholy Jacques outlines what he sees as the seven ages of man and his viewpoint that:

- "All the world's a stage"
- "all men and women have their exits and their entrances"
- "and one man in his time plays many parts"

With this sort of outlook, whatever our age and stage of life, we can enjoy:

- looking forward.
- learning from what we have done and where we have been.
- taking the knowledge and experience we have acquired, and our insight and understanding.
- achieving a maturing of outlook and the application of accumulated wisdom for the benefit of patients, colleagues and ourselves.

The word doctor comes after all from the Latin word with the same spelling and meaning 'teacher'. Indeed, there is much as health professionals we all learn and from what of this we assimilate, we can pass on to in turn, help others. The poem, Fostering Vision is intended to illustrate the key points.

Fostering Vision

We are taught and learn from the experience of others
to look for ourselves and examine what's there,
to see what's being shown and from the seeds being sown
to think for ourselves, to mean what we say and say what we mean,
to become better tuned, to hear what is said and learn what can be done,
to take part in what happens and with all that's around,
to care about others and think of their needs;

We are taught and learn with our eyes and our ears,
to then in our thoughts and our deeds,
read and study, explore and examine
research and inquire, audit, critique and review
all we do and what we have done and with that we are judging
continue to broaden our outlook and deepen our drive;

As it is both in our work and our lives
that others have given and do give us their trust,
we need for them and to better ourselves,
go on fostering our vision and opening our minds,
keeping abreast, remaining aware and eager to learn,
showing that we do listen, can and will help
and that we continue to care.

13 Inter-Personal Energy Flows and Responsibility (Response-Ability)

This section is about situations that apply to interactions with patients, staff, colleagues, friends, and our loved ones amongst others.

Where attention goes, energy flows
Attention is an energy flow. When we pay attention to someone, we send them positive (and maybe sometimes negative) energy. This is known by people, young and old, and marketing managers throughout the world.

Energy flows consist of attention + weather. Weather is the emotional content of the attention.

As one of my patients, Christopher, once said to me: “Some people carry some pretty strange weather and they’re very happy to share it or even throw it at you!”

Paying attention to the other person is a very powerful thing to do. Active listening is a skill to be practiced (not just hearing the words, but hearing the feelings and the deeper truth and concerns behind the words as well as observing what is not said as well as what is said).

Attention Exercise
Let’s now look an exercise which helps us understand that attention is a flow of energy.

In pairs, choose one person who will talk, and one who will listen. The talker can just tell a story about anything for 60 seconds. The listener is invited to listen attentively for the first 30 seconds, using non-verbal communication (but no words or noises).

At the sound of a signal (bell or chime), the listener remains silent, but deliberately pays zero attention to the speaker. For the next 30 seconds, the listener withdraws all attention, looking away.Then repeat exercise, the other way around.

Discuss experiences - Usually people find that the talk really flows fluently when attention is given, and becomes very difficult, stopping and starting (like walking through sticky mud) when attention is withdrawn. The first half feels easy and flows whereas the second half feels really hard-going.

The conclusion we can draw from this is that attention is real energy flow, and facilitates fluency. Where Attention Goes, Energy Flows. **WAGEF**

Energy Flows

When an energy flow comes towards us, we only have four choices. We can either:

- Accept
- Deflect
- Reflect (not always advised!)
- Change or transmute it

Energy flows can be described as positive uplifting ones (love, appreciation, gratitude) or negative down pulling ones (hate, fear, anger, blame, guilt).

Some of these can evoke the same, or complementary ones in us For example: love towards me may make me feel love, and reflect it. Anger towards me may make me feel angry back, or guilty, or fearful.

(Transference is the sending of an energy flow, counter-transference is being aware of what feelings a received energy flow evoke in oneself).

Why is this important? Well, energy flows can be shared, and always work down a diffusion gradient, from more to less. So even if you start the day really positive, by interacting (and being empathetic to) maybe twenty patients, you can absorb their weather and feel exhausted. Furthermore, when they leave, they want to see you again next week (at least they do if you are a friend or their GP and easily accessible)!

By the end of a clinic you can feel drained; because you have been, literally! (That's why it's important to have sources that can refresh you, and reconnect you with a source of energy: pictures of nature, landscapes, favourite activities, loved ones, and others can all fulfil this need).

13.1 What happens when people meet?

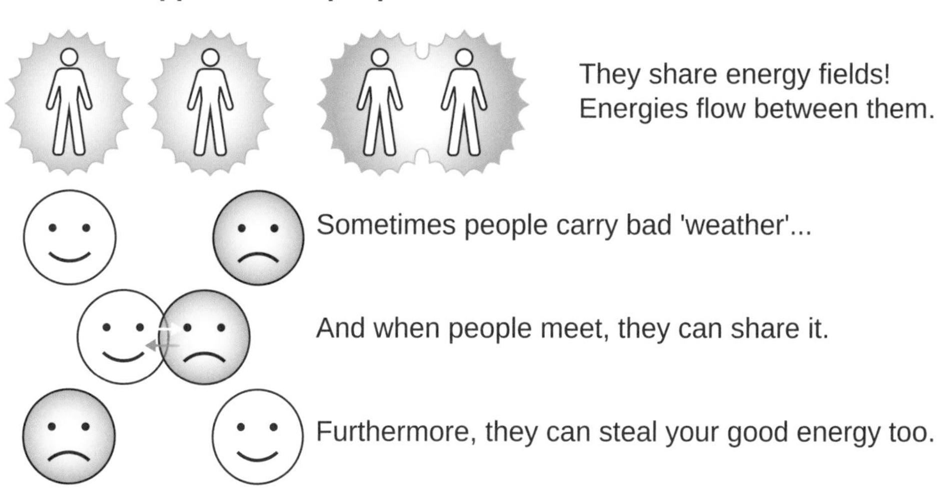

13.2 Weather and Energy Flows

When an energy flow comes towards us, we have 4 options:
(In this case the energy flow is anger, represented by a red arrow.)

1. **Accept it**

Often, if you accept a negative energy, it will dampen your mood

2. **Reflect it**

If you reflect a negative energy (like a mirror) then you will act negatively as well.

3. **Deflect it**

The energy shoots past you, not having any affect.

4. **Transmute it**

You change energies with tact, diplomacy or humour.

Weather and Energy Flows

Absorbing other peoples' weather is optional - we can choose just to observe. Remember, we have choices:

1. **Accept** (and absorb) the energy flow. This is fine if it's a really nice sunny one but if it's a dark and gloomy one, you might want to use an umbrella or raincoat! (This is especially true if you are in the 20% of really sensitive people who can feel the atmosphere of a room).

3. **Reflect** is not advised to counter anger or frustration! In the consulting room it is better to be supportive yet neutral, and to observe. Reflecting anger back may be very unprofessional, as is projecting it inappropriately in the first place. (Remember anger transformed is creativity. So don't let people stay angry, help them get creative!)

2. **Deflect**.This requires us to imagine that we have an umbrella, a shield, or a golden bubble that just stops other peoples' weather getting to us . The weather, or energy flow, can then move elsewhere to be recycled by nature. (Some people visualise other peoples' energy flow bypassing them and going harmlessly elsewhere). A variation is to imagine a balloon between the two of

you. This balloon absorbs any negative energy coming at you from the other person and safely contains it. When you are ready, you just ask the balloon to either sink down into the ground, or float far away into the sky, to be recycled by nature.

4. **Change the energy or weather**. This requires care but can be very effective. The safest way is to radiate positive support, encouragement and kindness. Less safe, but sometimes effective is humour such as 'black humour' as used in the emergency services or military. This, or just normal humour can result in laughter which literally 'gets it off our chest'. Curiously, the chest movements of laughing and sobbing are very similar, with similar effects of dissipating a stuck state of weather. It gets stuff 'off our chest' - literally! Beware using ANY humour at all in the consulting room; patients often think you are laughing at them, not with them. You have to know someone well to be able to share humour and the 'power gradient' must be flat.

Sending Energy

Whenever we speak to someone (or at a quantum level even think of them), we send them attention, which is a form of energy. When we use words, we can either send them with positive uplifting energy, or with negative energy that depletes their vitality. It seems as though we have choices with our words: we can either bless or we can curse, depending upon our intention. So, we have to conclude that:

Words are like spells, so cast them with care!

Even thinking negative thoughts towards someone else can be harmful! New research is also showing us how negative thoughts affect our own health just as much as the person we are thinking about. So selfishly, for our own health, we need to be peaceful inside and to cultivate goodwill to others. Wow – that's a really big one for society… We may have to mature beyond childhood emotions towards others. Forgiveness is actually a selfish act - it helps one person most of all - because the one who forgives is the one benefits the most!

The 4 P's of Prolonged Eye Contact

Seduction is something we all learn well, as babies! We need to se-duce (Latin: se-duco, to lead to ourselves) the caring adult to ensure that we have food, warmth, nurture and so that we survive. Some of us never quite lose these needs or strategies.

A glance across a room could mean that a meeting of minds should take place. However, prolonged eye contact can be uncomfortable; respectful attention will usually break gaze to avoid discomfort.

What can prolonged eye contact mean? It means attention because of interest.

It may be:

- Passion - this can include genuine respect, adoration, love, or deep interest
- Persuasion - a sales pitch
- Predation - animal intent (maybe including relationship/sexual connotations), or as adversary; imminent attack
- Pleading - as in for help if sad or even suicidal

Consider the fixed eyes of frozen grief; the pleading eyes of desperation; the insistent stare of convincing truths.

One Two, Three

In any relationship, conversation, or other 'energy transaction', there are always four things going on. We always see things from our own point of view. Furthermore, as we are seeing the other person, we often think that what's going on is 'Their stuff'. But actually there are always four dynamics:

1. My stuff
2. Joint stuff
3. Your stuff
4. Outside stuff (fire alarm, thunder, sunshine etc.)

Just take the phrase: "You make me so angry" and think about it! Whose stuff is that? You might think that it's your stuff. No way! It's my stuff because what is really happening is this:

1. You are performing an action (it may be just being there)
2. I am observing that action
3. That action is causing a reaction in my software
4. The response I am choosing to have is anger

So who is responsible? Actually, it's my stuff and my responsibility. You see, Responsibility = Response + Ability = Ability to choose my Response. Definitely 'my stuff'! (Oops!)

(This little interplay shows that we often lack insight into our own emotional state or coping strategies – in this case, Projection of our issues onto someone else, so that we pretend to our selves that 'they' are responsible, not 'us').

You see, we all have choices about our actions and reactions and choices have consequences! We also have Responsibility = Response + Ability. Sometimes, it's not your stuff, or my stuff, or joint stuff, but it's 'what's outside'. However, we still have the ability to choose our response!

Responsibility in Self-Care

Perhaps you'd like to consider whose responsibility is it to look after illness? Whose responsibility is it to look after health? Whose responsibility is your own health?

A notice on Australian GP's Door reads:

"Your Health is our Concern - but Your Responsibility!"

Sensitive Souls - Empathy and Sensitivity

All of us have a 'software being' as well as a 'hardware body'.

Have you ever felt things didn't feel right; had a really good or bad feeling about someone or something; been able to relate easily to people or felt other people's pain? Then you are empathic and perceptive.

Empathy is a fantastic tool. However, it is largely an unconscious skillset which, when left unguarded and unguided, makes us vulnerable to absorbing as well as observing. It is a valuable skill to know when something doesn't feel right but if we absorb negative emotions from the environment or from others, these can overwhelm us. The Strength of Sensitivity by Kyra Mesich[1] is groundbreaking. Empathic people (about 20% of the population) should all read it.

Empathy misunderstood or not taught fully leaves us vulnerable - a bit like a conscious choice of going outside in the pouring rain with no umbrella or raincoat and hoping not to get wet!

The positive sides of sensitivity, Kyra tells us, are:

1. Acute sensory processing.
2. Powerful emotions.
3. Effective and more brain activity in response to stimuli.
4. Strong autonomic body responses: gut, heart and other.
5. Quick reactions in nervous system.
6. Empathy, conscientiousness and compassion.
7. Creativity and appreciation of art, nature and beauty.
8. Perception of environmental and other people's energies.
9. Intuition, with good gut instincts.
10. Love of and feeling of connection with nature.

Kyra reminds us that empathic communication is in the quantum field of soul. It happens instantaneously, and transcends distance. The feelings can range from subtle to blatant.

A keen psychotherapist, she began to suffer from strange emotional states, such as distress, anxiety or an unexplained dark feeling. Curiously, she noticed that after feeling these states, a client would present with exactly the same feelings. The penny dropped : she realized that she was unconsciously absorbing other people's emotions even at a distance.

Many people use empathy all the time; it is a valuable tool and skill that complements the intellect. We use it to 'suss out' what the other person is feeling, and it guides us in our developing relationships. Empathic people also tap into the web of consciousness - so coincidences manifest - such as your friend ringing from abroad - just after you thought of them. Empathy is a tool which observes emotional vibes from the surroundings and from other people. However, this sensitivity needs guarding, otherwise we not only observe, but absorb as well. If we absorb other peoples' stuff we have to deal with that as well as our own stuff. If it's overwhelming, it's only too easy to palliate it by throwing it at someone else, using alcohol to blot our emotions, chocolate to comfort, shopping to soothe us (or other methods!).

In order to help us feel safe and stop us absorbing 'stuff' as well as observing, we can use boundaries like a 'shield' or a 'golden bubble' - mental constructs to keep us safe within a bubble away from other peoples' weather. Many people find that these are helpful. In addition, Kyra Mesich found that Yarrow Flower Essence builds a powerful psychic shield. How many of us in the healing field - or as mothers, fathers or in our other roles in life have our empathy unguarded? What difference would it make if it was less vulnerable?

The answer is that we are then empowered - we have choices and we are in control. Kyra's book has several exercises to explore ourselves and guide us to understand empathy. We can Observe - Not Absorb. **ONA**. Furthermore, we can respect our own boundaries.

From Inner Stillness and Inner Safety come Effective Action. **ISEA.**

Empathy understood is powerful because we can then tune in to our 'intuition'; our 'in-tune station', or our 'inner tutor'. This is powerful because we then know the answers as true - not because someone else has told us. One powerful coaching question to 'still' our self, and then ask is: 'What is it that I now know that I need to do next?' and another: 'If I were to know the answer, what would it be?'

As Mesich states: *"Maybe the Meek can Inherit the Earth - because they can attune to and ride the flows and patterns of life."*

What is more, I believe, every one of us can learn to still ourselves, to tune in to who we are and how we feel and to know answers that our logical mind cannot access. We all know how, the harder you try to think of something, the further away you drive the answer. Relax and often the answer can just pop into your head. Or, by coincidence (!) you wake up with the answer after a sleep.

The challenge for society is to acknowledge empathy and the skillset of sensitivity. What's more, these are attributes first and foremost of 'software being', or soul which force us to recognize that not only are we each mind, body and soul, but also that we are all connected in the 'quantum field' of the world. A truth that might just meet some resistance…

Protection

Protection is two fold. First is having boundaries, second is having no unresolved personal issues that allow others to press a 'hot button' in you.

Boundaries can be enhanced by visualising or creating imaginary walls, so that each of us has our 'own space', safe from others. Some people enhance this feeling of safety by placing a golden bubble around themselves; some just 'know' that nothing can touch or affect them. Others, not knowing about healthy boundaries, see other people as threatening or irritating. Neither judgment is fair; it is just an external projection of the need to enhance our own healthy safe boundaries! If you go out into the rain, you expect to get wet - unless you use an umbrella or a raincoat - so why do we expose ourselves to other peoples' weather, and then are surprised when we re affected by that weather?

If we react to a stimulus (an energy flow), then either our boundaries have been breached, or we have our own inner issues that are awaiting resolution.

Exercise

If I were teaching a group of teenagers, I would invite them to do the following:

Please sit comfortably, and look at the pen I am holding. Imagine it is someone you've never met, who is a bit angry with you.

Notice where you feel this - Is in your brow, face, throat, chest or stomach?

Try to 'switch off' the pen, and let the feeling disappear. (For most people, it quickly drops away, for a few people it remains stuck – these people are retaining the static charge, and need a 'Grounding Legs' sequence to help release the static).

Now, imagine that around you, half a metre from your body, is a 'golden bubble'. You may prefer a 'shield' or 'cloak'. It may have a colour, and a texture. It may spin very fast or it may be still, but what it does do is stop everybody else's weather hitting you and being absorbed. It's self – cleansing and it works at 1000% (why settle for 100%!). Moreover, it works for ever to keep you safe from other peoples' unpleasant weather.

Would you like one of these? (Everybody says 'yes'). Then would you like to ask for it? If you imagine it, see it, feel it, know it then it's yours!

We then repeat the exercise with the pen and everybody usually realises they now have something to protect themselves from other peoples' intrusive weather. Finally, in true Harry Potter style, I ask them to 'uncurse' the pen - otherwise (I say) I cannot be responsible for what it writes next!

Remember: Where Attention Goes, Energy Flows. **WAGEF**

There are also software tools such as flower essences that can enhance our boundaries, to be learnt about in future. (One well known one is Bach Walnut, another is Yarrow). However, this is outside the scope of this section. How many of us in the healing field or as mothers, fathers or in our other roles in life have our empathy unguarded? What difference would it make if it was guarded? Nobody has to stand in the rain without an umbrella or raincoat. It's good to observe - but not to absorb - other peoples' weather. **ONA** - Observe, not Absorb.

Some people also need to ground the 'static electricity' of unresolved emotion held within the software being system. Acupressure points on the legs can often help this - though be careful with these in pregnancy. Spleen10, Spl9, Spl6, Bladder57, GallBladder40, Kidney1 held on both legs with firm thumb pressure is one sequence; there are others. (Hint, the points are usually sore. NOT to be used in pregnancy).

Another grounding technique for the Software Being is to ask our Chakras (energy centres) to be balanced, harmonized and aligned. A few seconds on each, in this order, seems to work well: Still yourself - feet flat on floor, spine comfortable, slow regular diaphragmatic breaths: Base, Sacral, Solar Plexus, Chakra, Throat, back to Base, (pause), Earth Star Chakra, then back to Base, harmonise, balance and align. (see p20 for the diagram).

Reflection points:

- What does WAGEF stand for?
- What four things can you do with an energy flow coming towards you?
- What happens if you do not take control of energy flows?
- If you imagine someone upset with you, where do you feel it in your body?
- Have you ever projected your feelings at someone else?
- Whose responsibility is your own health?
- Are you empathic? Do you feel other peoples' emotions or those from a particular place?
- If so, how do you guard your sensitivity from becoming overwhelmed?

Dr Andrew Tresidder and Dr Zoe Fox

In Games People Play[1] Eric Berne tells us about **Transactional Analysis**. (A great read for all health professionals).

TA is based on three concepts that set it apart from mainstream psychology:

1. People are born OK.
2. People in emotional difficulties are nevertheless full, intelligent human beings.
3. All emotional difficulties are curable, given adequate knowledge and the proper approach.

He postulated that everyone begins life from the healthy position of "I'm OK, you're OK", that we all begin as little princes and princesses and are only turned in to frogs by our early experiences in life.

14.1

You are okay with me

I am not okay with me		I am okay with me
I am not OK **You are OK** The 'one-down' position *"I wish I could do as well as you do."*	**I am OK** **You are OK** The 'healthy' position *"Hey, we're making good progress now."*	
I am not OK **You are not OK** The 'hopeless' position *"Oh, this is terrible - we'll never make it."*	**I am OK** **You are not OK** The 'one-up' position *"You're not doing that right - let me show you."*	

You are not okay with me

Intimacy

All human beings crave intimacy; a connection to life and often to other people. As small children, we especially need attention and nurture. The unit of attention Dr Berne calls a 'stroke', and by the giving or withholding of strokes, we are domesticated, like puppies and kittens, into acceptable patterns of behaviour. Small mammals, deprived of love and affection, can die even if fed and watered; humans develop dysfunctional behaviour instead. Through this domestication process of education, we are moulded by those who love us, those who teach us, and those who wish to manipulate us. Consequently, we absorb society's patterns of thinking, often unconsciously. Through this process, we may adopt certain patterns of behaviour to obtain strokes. On the whole we look for 'nice' strokes but also sometimes for 'nasty strokes'. You see, to be ignored is actually more painful than to be criticized. Sometimes, as a result, many of us become 'little pleasers'. A few of us may become 'little rebels'.

The wisdom of the young: As one seven year old child said to her parents on a walk at the seaside, when complimented upon her good behaviour: 'I don't have my big sisters here, so I don't have to play up to get your attention' - she was obviously an old soul who had already studied TA!

Persona

Each of us has three persona (aspects of personality): 'parent', 'adult' and 'child'. Our 'parent' can be wise and guiding or bossy and dominating, our 'adult' makes sensible decisions based on all the data and our 'child' can be free and creative (or whining and manipulative). It is up to us which state we choose to be in (and how to relate to other people).

Where is the 'power' held? We each carry our own power. In 'adult' we hold it and relate to others at an equal level (even if we are older, more senior, etc). In 'parent' we take not just our own power, but also that of the other, whilst in 'child' we give our power away! Some people get accustomed to taking the 'child' role, some 'parent' and so on.

When we relate to another person, an 'adult'-'adult' relationship is safe and fair with equality of power, whilst 'parent'-'child' and 'child'-'parent' involve unequal power dynamics. It is up to the 'parent' to use the 'power' entrusted to them wisely and to seek to help the 'child' grow into 'adult'. Finally, it's up to the 'child' NOT to manipulate.

The trouble is, as health professionals, (including senior ones) we are often attracted into the role of 'parent' by our patients, staff or other grades and worse still we may sometimes take the role too seriously!

The danger of taking any role is that we can unconsciously become tempted into the Drama Triangle... Health professionals may have considerable 'personal power' but often forget the vast quantity of 'role power' that society projects onto us.

Have you ever felt let down, upset, guilty, angry, frustrated, sad or hurt? Chances are, you may have been pulled into the Drama Triangle. The Drama Triangle is all about relationships - relationships with unequal power, and manipulation. Every dysfunctional interaction takes place around the

Drama Triangle.

Good consultations ensure effective communication. However, there are some simple factors that are easily overlooked, that can easily turn a good consultation into a poor one. A series of dysfunctional consultations can lead to physician exhaustion and burnout. If we want good communication, then we must be aware of the Seat of Power and the Drama Triangle, and the Five Agreements.

The Seat of Power and the Drama Triangle

"Every profession is a conspiracy against the layman"

said George Bernard Shaw in The Doctor's Dilemma[2] using a heavy dose of irony. This may apply in some consultations but for this example, we will imagine a meeting between Doctor and Patient.

> Two people approach a consultation, both independent adults. The expert knowledge lies with the professional. However, the layman, through lack of knowledge, fear or anxiety, may (sometimes) give away his/her power of autonomy. It is up to the professional to share the power as much as possible or at any rate, only to use it wisely for the patient, and then to hand it back, finishing the consultation with both people as independent adults once more. Otherwise, patient and physician enter the Drama Triangle of relationships.[3]

Nearly all patients take the role of adult by looking for a sensible solution and appropriate support. Just occasionally, patients (or health professionals!) may feel anxious, fearful or worried and take a child role - which if taken to extremes, is a 'victim state'. **PLEASE NOTE THAT THE HIGHEST ROLE OF THE PROFESSIONAL IS TO RECOGNISE ANY IMBALANCES AND ALWAYS TO GUIDE THE CLIENT / PATIENT BACK TOWARDS ADULT.**

This explanation is to help us understand psychology as it works; it is about avoiding any blame culture by understanding, and creating a supportive 'appreciation culture'.

Furthermore, please note that this analysis ONLY applies to the occasional difficult consultation or interaction. The majority of your interactions will go smoothly, be 'game-free' and go nowhere near the Drama Triangle. Still, it's worth knowing about the issue, in case it traps you unawares.

The Drama Triangle has three roles: one 'child', and two 'parent'. The 'child' can give away their power to a 'parent', and can play 'victim', using the script: "If you help me / save me / protect me, I will give you my power (and my approval)". The person playing 'parent' (very often the physician) takes the power and becomes 'rescuer' (health professionals go into medical roles to help people get better). The underlying assumption may run "If you give me your power, I will protect and help you (as long as you also give me your approval)". The unspoken dilemma is that often the health professional's inner 'child' may crave the approval of the patient's 'parent'. This is an unstable dynamic. Unfortunately, in the patient's eyes, there are only two types of health professional: good and bad or even 'the best in the world' and 'rubbish'.

Beware when you hear words like "you're a good doctor, you're such a good doctor, you're a wonderful doctor" because you may be entering the Drama Triangle. Even worse, you may be being seduced by well-meaning flattery into standing upon a rising pedestal until the patient decides to change their approval to criticism, WITHOUT THE HEALTH PROFESSIONAL DOING ANYTHING DIFFERENT…

And what happens to people on pedestals? They can fall or be pushed off…

What is the difference between the two types of health professional (the best in the world and the worst)? Half a second, because that's how long it takes the patient (who unconsciously took the role of victim) to change their mind about the health professional (who unintentionally took the role of 'rescuer'), take back their power, and change role into 'persecutor'

"You nasty person, you took my power and abused me, now I'm going to abuse you".

14.2 The Drama Triangle

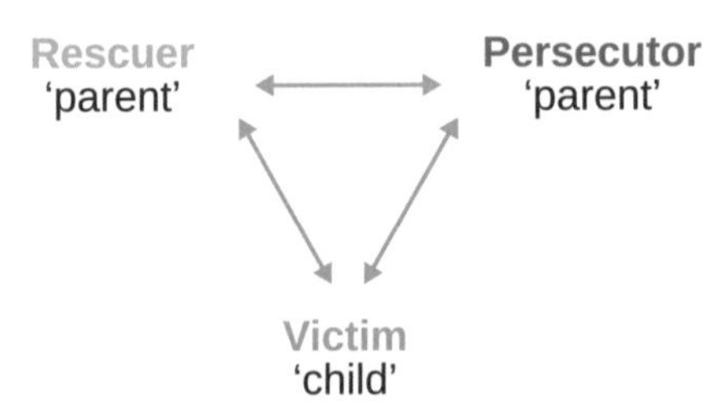

It is very easy to be enticed into, and then chased around, this triangle of dependency. When people use the triangle as a life script or when a patient sees the illness (cancer, pain, any other condition, or death) as 'persecutor', the health professional as 'rescuer' and him/herself as 'victim' – you can see that everyone is doomed to failure in this scenario. Nobody can win!

It may take considerable skill for the physician to help lift the patient out of the 'child' role of 'victim', yet can be part of the most rewarding aspects of medicine.

Unconscious collusion in the Drama Triangle is emotionally draining and may lead towards health professional burnout. It certainly leads to mutual patient and physician dissatisfaction. An understanding of these dynamics can illuminate consultations and help avoid both complaints and emotional exhaustion. Emotional exhaustion in the care-giver can lead to self-medication or other dysfunctional coping strategies.

Worst of all, professionals can easily be trapped into persecuting fellow professionals, especially if they are of a different 'tribe', - think: physicians vs surgeons; ward-based doctors vs emergency department, pathology or radiology; 'the juniors'; 'the management' - or 'the complementary therapists'. Beware: this trap is very easy to fall into. The answer of course here is honest communication and understanding. Interestingly, both acupuncture and homeopathy have had tough times to different degrees from Western-based thinking but this is partly because to understand them needs an understanding of information and physics, not the narrative of chemistry that pervades orthodox pathology and therapeutics. "Different tribe? Let's persecute them!" (Alternatively, we could choose to act as wise adults and grow beyond these games).

The worst engagement in the Drama Triangle is if the health professional starts to 'blame the patient', rather than understand them. We see this sometimes in cases of Medically Unexplained Symptoms (MUS). Actually, MUS means the medical framework of understanding is insufficient to explain the patient's condition. Perhaps MUS = Mis-Understood Symptoms.

So how do we get out of the Drama Triangle? Be true to ourselves (which means Knowing Ourselves), use the Five Agreements, and understand the Drama Triangle fully.[3] We'll look at these in sections 15 (p78) and 17 (p87).

In Hamlet, Shakespeare said: *"To Thine Own Self Be True".*

Love Supports, Criticism Withers LSCW

One of Aesop's fables tells the story of the boy who was swimming. The river current swept him into danger. In difficulties, he cried out for help. A proud self-righteous man called back "You stupid boy, what a dangerous place to swim." The boy replied "Please sir, can you rescue me first, and tell me off once I'm safe on dry land?"

The Empowerment Dynamic (TED – David Emerald)

The key to getting off the triangle is to move from external referencing (i.e. looking outside of ourselves for approval) to internal referencing (i.e. getting in touch with our authentic self, who has the answers, solutions, love, happiness and identity we choose for ourselves).

A Victim must stop looking for someone or something external to themselves to fix them, to give them the answers or to give them the love and support they need. A Rescuer must stop trying to change, control or get support from helping others. Both must learn how to love, honour, support and respect themselves. Persecution (blaming others) only results in greater negativity and never achieves anything positive. We all need to improve our attitudes towards change, control, risk and responsibility. We need to reframe our perspective to view life as a grand adventure rather than something of a chore to be endured. Above all we need to find the courage to admit that we are imperfect but still appreciate all of our individualities for the benefits they bring.

Dave Emerald developed a polarity map of the Drama Triangle which he called The Empowerment Dynamic, which suggests moving to the positive pole of the interpersonal dynamic by challenging instead of persecuting, coaching instead of rescuing and creating rather than being a victim.

Reconnecting to our dreams and desires; taking action forward towards those outcomes can require a major shift in mindset for many people but can result in greater awareness of ourselves and more options available to us.

The Empowerment Dynamic also has three roles - all adult.

The Creator is the central role and taps in to an inner state of passion. Directed by intention, it focuses on a desired outcome, propelling the creator to take small steps towards whatever it is that they want to create. The Creator owns their own ability to choose their response to life (takes response-ability).

The Coach uses compassion and questions to help the creator develop their vision and action plan. The Coach provides encouragement and support in place of "rescuing' actions.

The Challenger is focused on learning and growth, holding The Creator accountable while encouraging learning, action and next steps. The Challenger consciously builds The Creator up, as a positive alternative to putting someone down by criticising, blaming or controlling.

Shown in this format, you can see how The Empowerment Dynamic is the positive mirror image of The Drama Triangle:

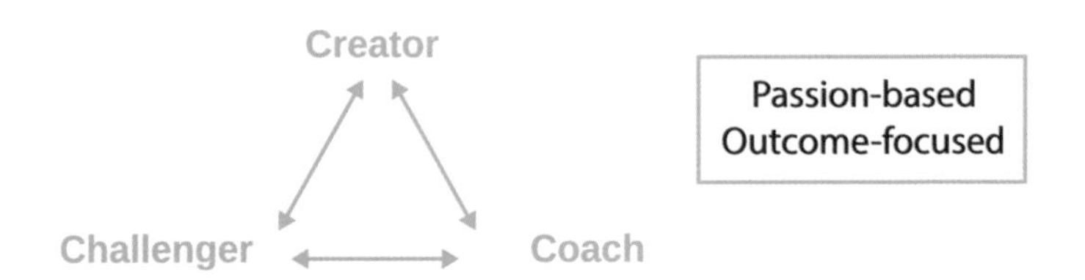

14.3 The Empowerment Dynamic

14.4 The Drama Triangle

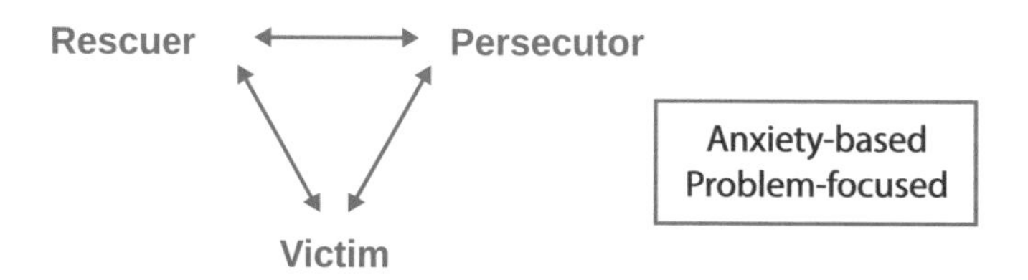

So, be aware of the Drama Triangle playing out in life, and in your consultations with patients. Do not allow boundary infringement or trespass to become boundary violation. Remember that at the end of the day, the health professional is **never** the patient's friend, no matter how friendly the relationship.

Six Questions to Answer in the Consultation that make you look clairvoyant and brilliant.

Every patient has these six questions, rarely uttered but always thought:

1. What is it?
2. Why me?
3. Why now?
4. What's going to happen?
5. What can you do about it?
6. What can I do about it?

Notice that the first five may occur in an 'adult' to 'adult' or a 'parent' to 'child' transaction but a good response to number six is definitely 'power sharing' and uplifting of 'child' into 'adult'.

Learning Resource

The appendix has a role play scenario to clarify The Drama Triangle (p178).

Reflection points:

- Can you see where the Drama Triangle has ever played a part in your work life?
- Can you see where the Drama Triangle has ever played a part in your personal life?
- How easy is it to help patients move into a competent adult role? What aids, resources and information could be used to help this?
- Think upon a situation where the Drama Triangle was resolved successfully...
  - What insights came to bear?
  - Where did kindness and compassion play a part?

15 The Drama Triangle: Gill Edwards' Insights[1]

Every dysfunctional interaction takes place around the drama triangle. It involves blocked or distorted communication based upon fear, judgment and insecurity. Whenever you feel disempowered, guilty, stuck, resentful, blaming, helpless, trapped, dependent, misunderstood, bewildered, betrayed, controlled, manipulated or abused, you are in a drama triangle - which might involve two, three or more people. At the top of the triangle are the one-up positions (parent), while at the bottom is the one-down position (child). Although many people have a familiar position, the roles can rotate with lightning speed, playing all the toxic games of codependency. There are no winners in a drama triangle. Everyone loses & feels like a victim - until someone stops playing the game.

15.1

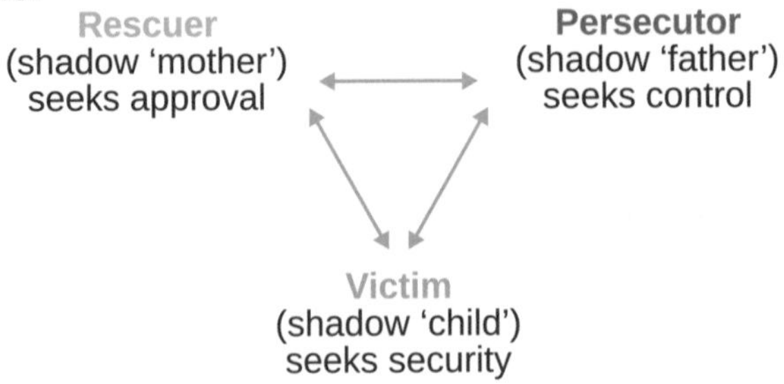

Rescuer
(shadow 'mother')
seeks approval

Persecutor
(shadow 'father')
seeks control

Victim
(shadow 'child')
seeks security

Dysfunctional relationships rotate constantly around the drama triangle, resulting in:

1. Pervasive sense of guilt and shame.
2. Lies, pretence and unhealthy secrets.
3. Manipulation, control and power.
4. Blaming and resentment.
5. Feelings of 'entitlement'.
6. Misguided loyalty which promotes lying/abuse.
7. Perceived lack of freedom.
8. Chaos, crisis and drama.
9. Scapegoating.
10. Denial of problems.
11. 'Protecting' others from facing their issues (also known as enabling).
12. Inappropriate sense of responsibility for others' feelings, needs or well-being.
13. Feelings of helplessness, worthlessness and inadequacy.
14. Distancing and avoidance of conflict in relationships.
15. Superficial conversations which avoid issues or repeated cycles of rage/blame/abuse/guilt then denial.

16. Fear of change - with desperate attempts to avoid change or maintain stability.
17. Inability to express emotions in healthy, empowering and responsible ways which increase intimacy.
18. Relative absence of healthy, loving and intimate interactions, or joy, freedom, creativity and spontaneity. Codependent/dysfunctional relationships tend to repeatedly hook in a third 'player' - a process known as triangulation - either as a common point of concern (eg. sick child or needy friend/parent), a common enemy to unite against, or a Rescuer who might become labelled a Persecutor. This third person/issue serves the purpose of 'distance regulation' to avoid real intimacy or more threatening issues. For some couples, an ex-partner serves this function; or they attract one 'lame dog' or worthy cause after another to focus on.

Two common rules in dysfunctional systems:

1. Pretend everything is fine (ie. don't be honest/authentic).
2. Don't threaten the status quo.

Persecutor

- Get to feel safe by hurting, criticising, controlling or abusing others.
- False sense of superiority or arrogance (which sometimes collapses into shame/insecurity of Victim).
- Want to be in control; might manipulate, use unspoken threats, ignore or bully others into submission.
- Self-righteous, judgmental and blaming; need to be seen as perfect and beyond reproach.
- Strong need to be 'in the right' and to see others as 'in the wrong'.
- Get adrenaline rush from being angry/righteous - so need an enemy to battle against.
- Can justify and defend their abusive or controlling behaviour.
- Feel 'entitled' to have others meet their needs, or to behave as they wish them to.

(This is the hardest pattern to acknowledge in ourselves. Chronic Persecutors are the least likely of the three to recognise their own issues or to seek help/ growth. Can be borderline personalities.)

Rescuer (or 'hero'/'martyr', or 'responsible parent')

- Get to feel safe/worthy by 'enabling' others - ie. bailing out, covering up for or protecting others.
- Believe they know what is best for other people, what is 'right' or what others should do.
- See themselves as wiser, stronger or more resourceful; might hand out

money, moralistic advice or guidance.
- Foster dependency or helplessness in others; disempower others by taking 'parental' role.
- Over-responsible for others' feelings/needs; avoid looking at own feelings/ problems by focussing on others.
- Anxiety-driven; often 'bound by loyalty' to dysfunctional relationships or situations.
- Proud of their caretaking (and might make a full-time job or profession of it).
- Feel guilty if not caring enough for others; tend to deny and sacrifice their own needs for others.
- Often feel like martyrs - over-burdened or unappreciated; play game of "After all I've done for you…"

Victim

- Get to feel safe by being submissive, giving in or being dependent/helpless.
- Blame other people, circumstances or past decisions for how they feel.
- Expect others to solve their problems for them - to 'rescue' them; often play 'Yes but…' games. **WDYYB** - see next section 'Games that get Played'.
- Passive, child-like dependency; find it hard to make decisions for themselves.

How to Escape the Drama Triangle

- Hold on to knowing that you are a good, worthy and loving person - and so are they.
- Take responsibility for your own feelings, and use your emotional guidance.
- Insist that others take responsibility for their own feelings (and their own lives).
- Stop shaming/blaming yourself or others, whatever the circumstances.
- Stop caring what anyone else might think of you, or trying to control others (ie. mind your own business).
- Insist that people treat each other (and you) with respect and compassion.
- Befriend your Shadow (so that you don't have to project it on to others).
- Pull back from relationships which are critical, abusive or manipulative - and look at how you attract that.
- Stop bailing others out, protecting them or trying to help 'lame ducks'.
- Don't get hooked into power games; engage only in honest and direct communication.
- Recognise the 'family-ar' (familiar) games you play, and catch yourself from slipping into those patterns.

Drama triangles are highly seductive and controlling; even when you recognise that games are being played, it can be difficult to opt out! When you stop playing in the drama triangle, others are likely to get angry, accuse you of being selfish, or even be abusive; or they might feign helplessness and fall into 'victim' mode. This is an attempt to shame you back into your familiar role of 'rescuer' or 'victim', so resist it! Recognise what needs of yours are being met by the drama triangle - such as feeling in control, or trying to feel worthy, or feeling safe. Then make new and healthy choices based on love, self-empowerment and authenticity.

If you slip into being a 'persecutor':

- Give up the need to be right; recognise that everyone is in the right from their own perspective.
- Be honest with yourself, and listen to others with an open heart.
- Sit with vulnerable feelings, instead of 'acting out' from anger or fear.
- Stop justifying or defending being hurtful, critical, controlling or abusive.
- Let go of any feelings of entitlement, and set others free.

If you tend to be a 'rescuer':

- Stop basing your self-esteem on helping, caring for or protecting others.
- Focus on yourself and your own needs/issues, instead of focussing on others' needs.
- Stop justifying taking care of others; don't 'protect' anyone from facing uncomfortable feelings or issues.
- Notice how others use guilt/manipulation to control you.
- Don't collude with seeing anyone as helpless or a victim; never take sides in a drama.
- Be responsible only for yourself and your feelings - and trust your own guidance; do what feels joyful.

If you tend to be a 'victim':

- Acknowledge your own strengths instead of looking for a Rescuer; think and problem-solve for yourself.
- Deal with your anger and learn to handle confrontation without giving in, rescuing or persecuting.
- Be authentic; stop pretending or manipulating. Take responsibility for your own needs and self-care.

Gill Edwards, 2007. Used for health teaching purposes with permission from 2010.

For further tips to escape the Drama Triangle, see The Five Agreements (P87).

16 Games That Get Played; Role Power and Attraction

Every health professional should read Games People Play by Eric Berne. It shows us how our own, and other peoples' behaviour, can cause all sorts of problems including wasting a lot of emotional energy. The purpose of 'games', of course, is self-justification at someone else's expense... To boost an insecure ego from someone else's attention...

Sadly, we can all get pulled into colluding with games sometimes. Here are three we might come across:

Why Don't You, Yes But - WDYYB

In one of Berne's archetypal games, the protagonist states that something isn't right. For example:

"This kitchen is so old-fashioned".

The onlookers then try to help: *"Why don't you buy a new one?"*

"Yes, but it's too expensive".

"Why don't you get your husband to make one?"

"Yes, but he hasn't got the tools."

"Why don't you buy him some tools?"

"Yes, but he doesn't know how to use them."

And so on...

You can see that the 'game' gives benefit to the protagonist, who always wins and gets a kick from the attention of the group! The only antithesis (healing resolution) is when the protagonist can be persuaded to spend their time in more worthwhile pursuits other than complaining.

In medicine this can happen when a needy patient complains of a symptom. (This is not referring to a physical illness). Subconsciously they are often intent on being paid attention rather than getting better. What then happens is that the GP tries to problem-solve and give a treatment. Each week the patient returns to the GP, no better, asking for a different treatment. Either the GP runs out of options, refers the patient to a colleague, or eventually realizes that the patient needs attention, not treatment. This is not an easy situation to manage and requires skills of people management and psychology.

In prison medicine this is sometimes seen when the patient returns three days after a prescription for an antidepressant saying it hasn't worked yet and demanding an alternative.

The counterpart game, sometimes played by Doctors, is:

I Was Only Trying to Help You - IWOTTHY

In this game, the patient keeps returning week after week, and is given a new treatment each time. Sooner or later, a treatment is given which has side effects, or worse still has fatal side-effects. You can easily see how a doctor would be trapped into this game, especially as when a treatment is prescribed with good intention, the side effects can often be minimized in the mind of the medical professional for this patient (he/she will benefit without harm this time).

Of course, should harm occur, the professional might try to justify themself by saying: *"I Was Only Trying to Help You"*.

The only honest antithesis to this game is to be aware of the temptations of over-treatment and of incorrect diagnosis.

It is easy to be trapped into a parallel game of '**blame the patient**' when the pathology of a new condition is not understood and mechanism is obscure. For instance: CFS/ME was initially attributed to psychological factors, ignoring the physical changes and mitochondrial dysfunction. It's so much easier to dismiss a medically unexplained condition as due to patient issues or some other explanation than it is to appreciate that say, a lack of nutritional knowledge, causes the whole medical profession to be handicapped in its understanding. Many are the serious illnesses that were once 'medically unexplained' including puerperal fever, Parkinsons, coeliac syndrome, pellagra and chronic fatigue syndrome.

Wooden Leg

Sometimes people play this game: "I'd love to do… but I can't because of my wooden leg" (or other disability).

Please note: nobody plays 'games' for fun. They are life positions and of course anyone is entitled to have a genuine disability. The 'games' come when there is secondary gain to be made from playing.

We can see the Drama Triangle behind a lot of these games.

Pig

Pig is the game of repeatedly asking for more information, advice, or input, in order to wear the other person down, possibly because of an old grudge (see Kipling's Plain Tales from the Hills). In 19th century British India 'A' is sold a bad horse by 'B'. 'A' then spends years steadily pursuing 'B' through requests for information about all aspects of pig farming and so on, which by the rules of the age, 'B' is compelled to answer. This eventually exhausts and frustrates 'B'. One day they meet and 'B' states his grievance; 'A' tells 'B' why he was trying to get his own back, and then takes him out to dinner - and of course stops the game.

Power as a Doctor or Professional

As medical professionals, we hold more power than we may realize. The two types of power are:

- Role power
- Personal power

Role power can also give situational power.

The aim, of course, is always to stand in one's own power and to empower others (with kindness and respect).

People are often attracted to 'power'. This is often a result of projected need, for example:

- I need parenting
- I need security
- I need friendship
- I need a mate
- You look like the son/daughter I wish I'd had
- You look like the father/mother I wish I'd had
- You look like the partner I wish I had

Professionals can also hold any of these needs subconsciously - "My stuff". If the professional remains unaware of (or blind to - see pp159-160) their own needs, they may lead to a boundary crossing. In fact:

Patient unmet needs + professional unmet needs *may lead to* unhealthy boundary crossings.

Role Power and Attraction in the Consulting Room

All professionals have two types of power: 'personal power' and 'role power'. The first comes from our personality and charm, how we dress, our consultation style, our compassion and friendliness and above all our self-belief and how we hold ourselves. The second, 'role power', is all about how other people see the role of the health professional and very little about what we project ourselves.

It is a fact of life that people are attracted to power. Often, as children we may have a special respect for and possibly relationship with a particular teacher. This can play out as an attraction in our adult lives.

It is part of our inner child looking to be validated (and loved) by a person in authority. As infants we are brilliant at charming (maybe seducing) adults into a relationship with our smiles and gurgles! Some of us never fully forget that ability.

A young woman was seen, recovering from depression. Her psychiatrist had wondered if there was a progression towards a 'high' mood. On the first occasion of consultation for a headache, the woman complimented the male GP on his tie and shirt. On the next visit she complimented his room and on the next asked when his birthday. Finally, she gave him a present of something she had made herself. She then asked him what his home address was and whether she could meet him outside work. She plainly had intentions… or at minimum had an unhealthy attachment, which might have developed into stalking.

The GP managed this with probity, discussing with partners, writing to the patient to explain the inappropriateness of the behaviour and noting that a chaperone would be needed for future consultations

After treatment of her mood disorder (she had indeed developed mild mania), a normal doctor-patient relationship was re-established.

As professionals, we need to be very aware of our boundaries and how people will seek attention, validation, and sometimes a special relationship.
How does this play out in the Consulting Room?
What could have been not just a 'boundary infringement' or 'trespass' could have developed into a 'boundary violation' if the GP had not remained alert and detached.

Had this developed, this could in some situations, have a disastrous result, with involvement of GMC (General Medical Council), and so on.

How is this avoided?

- Remain in control and able to observe yourself.
- Beware of flattery, or charm.
- Be aware of little presents, or of what may be behind them.
- Be aware that many people are needy and can project that need for relationship/love/friendship onto a kindly pleasant professional.
- Beware that patients may have fantasies about us or our bodies of which we are completely unaware.
- Beware that their projection may actually be because of mental illness.

When the chips are down, the doctor (or health professional) is never the patient's friend - the doctor is always the patient's doctor, however friendly the relationship is.

In Games People Play, Eric Berne delineates Transactional Analysis and shows some of the scenarios that may arise. Well worth a read once in your professional career!

Some of the 'games' that patients (or health professionals) may subconsciously play, often because of Role Power, are:

- I want you to be my special friend
- You are a very special doctor/patient
- You mean a lot to me
- You've always been around for me (I need you)
- Gee, you're wonderful professor [From Games People Play]
- You're the best doctor in town - and I've tried all the others

And between fellow professionals:

- We're on the same committee
- We've been friends for so many years
- I trust you more than anyone else
- You've always been a good friend
- We play golf / snooker (fill in the gaps) together
- We went to med school, high school, etc together (think of the pitfalls of Social Media leading to meeting an old flame)
- You remind me of…

This still allows normal social friendly interactive human behaviour - just be aware of the times when behaviour is nearing a 'boundary' and observe very carefully what is happening.

Healthy **boundaries** are important - they help us define ourselves, our limits and our behaviour with others. However, sometimes we can be tempted out of balance by our own needs, or by those of others into…

1. Boundary infringement
2. Boundary trespass
3. Boundary violation

Boundaries are physical, emotional, sexual, or regarding power. Exploitation can be financial, emotional, intellectual, sexual or through neglect (Coe Clinic for Boundaries Studies) - exploitation in therapy is the use or abuse for a client for personal gain. Fortunately this is rare, as professionals are usually aware of, and do not take advantage of these issues.

If, as health professionals as well as human beings, we are aware of potential problems, then we are unlikely to run into difficulties. If we are unaware, then without realising, we may find ourselves in difficulties.

17 Relationships 3: The Five Agreements, Listening and Attention

The Toltecs were native South Americans. They had a well-developed system of wisdom about life and how we should live it. It is said that key points were these 'agreements':

1. Be Impeccable with Your Word.
2. Take Nothing Personally.
3. Make No Assumptions.
4. Always Do Your Best.
5. Be Sceptical, but Learn to Listen.[1]

Be Impeccable with Your Word BIWYW
By this, is meant that your word is an affirmation of your intent; a casting out of your will into the world, reinforced by power. So, say only what you mean and speak with integrity. Don't waste the power of your word in idle gossip or putting yourself down. Use your word as a vehicle for the power of your will, for good, with love and truth. (If you lie, you're only lying to yourself).

Take Nothing Personally TNP
We are all part of an interconnected universe but we are each having our own experiences. My stuff is my stuff, yours is yours. So nothing you do is because of me - it's your stuff. How I interpret that is up to me but it is better to take nothing personally, for nothing in life is done personally. If I do take it personally then it is me that chooses to suffer! Try to see an issue from the other's point of view.

Make No Assumptions (To Assume makes an Ass out of You and Me) MNA
Ask the little question "Why?" often, and find clear answers for yourself. Express your wishes clearly to avoid misunderstanding. Communicate clearly with others to avoid needless emotions, mistakes and upsets.

Always Do Your Best ADYB
When you are present in yourself and stand in your power, you are the best you can be. In life, everything is always changing. If we just do our best, whatever the circumstances, we are expressing our selves with integrity. That way, we avoid self-criticism and regret. Avoid any emotional attachment to the outcomes of your efforts.

Be Sceptical, but Learn to Listen BSLL

People tell us their story - but it is from their perspective, not necessarily the whole view. When we learn to listen, we understand truth at a deeper level. Using the power of doubt allows us to discern the truth behind their words and communication. So it is important to use curiosity when assessing the story, asking ourselves 'Is it truth, or is it not? Is it reality, or is it a virtual reality?' Everything we all do is guided by a positive intention - try and find out what the other person's positive intention is, and life becomes a whole lot easier.

What's Going on Behind What's Going On? **WGOBWGO** ("One last question, please. Just help me understand why…" The 'Columbo Approach').

Listening

Listening has two main aspects: active and passive.

Listening is not the same as hearing.Hearing means noticing sounds, whereas listening means paying attention to what is heard. Many of us listen passively - waiting to interrupt - or thinking of what we wish to say next!

Active listening means stilling yourself, paying positive attention to the other person and being receptive to:

- What is said and how it is said.
- Body language and non-verbal communication (which may be at variance with the words).
- What is not said.
- The deeper meaning behind the words.

Alan Watkins[2] describes a MAP process:

1. 'Move' - your attention away from your thoughts and into your body, and breathe (rhythmically, regularly and slowly).
2. 'Appreciate' the speaker, 'bathing them in warm acceptance and unconditional positive regard'.
3. 'Play back' the underlying meaning to the other person, first as what you feel they communicated, and then as an offer or question (not an assertion).

Complaints

We can see that complaints often revolve around the Drama Triangle, and often relate to loss and grief, whether due to a death, a loss of health, or a loss of dreams and hopes. Complaints are often about facts, but are always driven by feelings. Managing complaints is an art.

It involves 'adult'-'adult' communication of the highest and kindest degree, all the while dealing with a hurt or grieving patient or relative (or occasionally with those very few people who just like complaining. Vexatious complaints are a different subject again).

It involves acknowledging the feelings (and apologizing for the distress or harm that occurred), addressing the facts in a non-judgmental way and looking to seek a resolution by providing answers.

A complaint may feel personal, but it isn't. (Please see the Five Agreements.) The reason complaints hurt health professionals, compared to some other professions, is because very often we take a 'parental' role towards our patients, accept thanks, and our 'inner child' is soothed and validated. So when we receive a complaint, it often wounds our inner child.

Besides, in life, we are all learning. Investigation of issues should always seek the learning, rather than finding fault and casting blame.

Remember: **Where attention goes, Energy flows.**

Attention is an energy flow. When we pay attention to someone, we send them positive (maybe sometimes negative) energy. This is known by people, young and old, and marketing managers through the world. (Question: who are the best at seduction? Babies are - they se-duce (lead to themselves) our attention - because they need it). NB, the word seduction here is free from anyconnotations, negative, sexual or other.

Energy flows consist of attention + weather. Weather is the emotional content.

Please put both feet on the ground; allow your spine to become upright and comfortable. Feel free to allow yourself to take three slow abdominal (diaphragmatic) breaths - slowly in and out. Notice how you feel - you have just introduced 'calm' into your body. Feel free to repeat this whenever you wish…

Reflection points:

- Which, for you, are the easiest of the Five Agreements to adopt?
- Which are the difficult ones?
- How would you go about personal change in the light of these?
- Have you ever had to deal with a complaint? How did you respond? Was it with respect?
- How would you deal with a complaint about a junior colleague responsible to you? (especially if you happen not to like them) - or a senior colleague who made you feel small?
- Is it easy to be seduced into the Drama Triangle when involved in complaints? If so, which role(s) and towards whom?

18 Trust, Culture and Risk

Alex Aylward.

Professional trust between colleagues, patients, departments, organisations, and the wider health care system needs continual attention, in order to maintain a safe working culture. This culture is fair to all, values staff, and allows clinicians to practise in their preferred ways best for patients.

Resource constraints and organisational changes can generate unmanageable workloads, and increase the risks of litigation, work/life imbalance, poor health and low morale. They can increase tensions between primary and secondary care, blur professional boundaries, cause clashes of values. This can lead to some people assessing their risks and opting to 'cut corners', whilst others do not. If you become aware of behaviour or performance (your own or others) falling below professional standards, you might be at risk of conflict or collusion and be co-creating a work culture that is unsafe.

Codes of Conduct are tools that increase clarity around professional boundaries. This helps maintain a supportive working culture that engenders trust. The codes are made from statements and rules generated and agreed by professionals on why, how, and what to do to operate effectively as a team and how to achieve desired outcomes. They can include how to handle differences or conflict. Ideally the codes are limited to less than 10 statements/rules. All members of the team need to agree and sign up to the Code of Conduct. This gives clarity and enables self-regulation, as anyone can call anyone else to account if a code is breached. Codes make expected behaviour, and hence results, explicit.

Remember, we all have preferences in the way we like to give and receive information i.e. visual, kinaesthetic, auditory, or any combination. Also, we have psychological working behaviour preferences e.g. being nurturing, directive, or analytical, or a combination of them, that we express differently in our normal natural state from our stressed state. Knowing our own preferences, and those of others, is helpful in understanding situations and relationships.

If you take risks that it impact on your trust with colleagues, it's important to find support. This support could be your appraiser, other organisational support, a clinicians' support group like a Balint group, all of which are safe places to get things 'off your chest'. You might consider coaching to help change/improve part of your work/life through.

A beautiful garden doesn't happen by accident - it requires care and attention. Trust is the same.

On Dealing with Difficult Colleagues RCPsych http://bit.ly/HaSC031

Dr Andrew Tresidder with contributions from Dr Zoe Fox and Alex Aylward.

What is 'life'? Who am I? What am I doing? We've already said that health is harmony of mind, body and spirit, so how we manage 'life's' journey has to be important. Are we passive participants, tossed about as victims of 'life', or active co-creators of our present and our destiny? Is 'life' lived outside-in or inside-out?

Let's look at some practical philosophy of 'life', see how it works and explain our journey through life. We'll also cover 'life's' Learning Cycle. Looking at these topics will empower us with understanding, so we can be 'in the driving seat'.

Who am I?

Some traditions encourage us to ask this question, and help us understand that:

- I am not my body
- I am not my emotions or my desires
- I am not my mind or my thoughts
- I am not my life story

Then who am I? Some sacred traditions would say that the real 'I' is the one who witnesses all of the above; body, emotions, thoughts, story, experiences and roles. The real 'I' is 'consciousness' which is observing, experiencing and working through us. 'Witness consciousness' is the ability to observe 'life' as it unfolds, as we each, as conscious beings, experience life, in roles, in relationships, in dramas and in events. Perhaps we are here to learn, to develop character and to grow? In essence, life is a journey of personal development. So, 'life' is a 'gift', inviting us forwards. 'Life' is by invitation! 'Life' takes us on a journey from birth till the present moment and continues until death. Death is when our consciousness leaves our physical body.

However, nobody tells us what life is about - sometimes it just seems that we muddle through. Certainly, we are always learning skills, knowledge and attitudes, as well as undergoing physical happenings and the wisdom we gain from our experiences. From childhood on, feeding, drinking, crawling, talking, walking, communicating, writing, reading, games, hobbies and sports are just a few of the things we learn - and sometimes grow beyond - as well as all our social experiences and our vocation in 'life'.

Knowing a little about how life works can help us on the journey, for 'LIFE' itself is an unbroken chain of evolution for at least two billion years that is coded for SUCCESS! It's only we humans that sometimes give ourselves a hard time when we find ourselves rushing frantically from beginning to end, worried about the future, pulled back by feelings from the past, without appreciating or even taking notice of the journey. And of course, what helps us so much of the time is 'support', which comes from within, from what happens around us, from others, and from 'LIFE' itself.

What is this life, if full of care, We have no time to stand and stare.

William Henry Davies[1]

Cautionary note: if you have any strong emotional reactions or irritation to any of the material in this section, try to stand outside yourself, to observe and to ask:

- Where does this reaction come from?
- What is it teaching me?
- Which of my personal or cultural hot buttons have been triggered?

Let's now share some simple thoughts about what makes people tick at an emotional level. You may already know nearly everything covered in this section, but we hope that the way we look at it together may give you new insights into how our lives work.

"The clock of life is wound but once,
And no man has the power
To tell just when the hands will stop
At late or early hour.

To lose one's wealth is sad indeed,
To lose one's health is more,
To lose one's soul is such a loss
That no man can restore.

The present only is our own,
So live, love, toil with a will,
Place no faith in 'Tomorrow',
For the clock may then be still."

Robert H Smith/Wilfred Grindle Conary (original author unresolved)

If we wish to be mature human beings in the 21st Century, there is a great opportunity to develop 'emotional intelligence'. We can raise our level of consciousness, grow beyond childish and immature patterns. Life then flows well. Raising consciousness to wiser levels of thought and action may be one of the most fulfilling things we can do in our lives. 'It is not what goes into a man that makes him unclean, it's what comes from his heart and his mind.'[2]

Just to remind ourselves: If you ask a hundred people how they are, what do they say? "Fine". But is it true? Of course not; it's our way of keeping to the surface issues in life, rather than admit to deeper unresolved issues. (FINE may stand for Fearful, Insecure, Neurotic and Emotionally imbalanced – or Feelings Inside Not Expressed - a fair description of what's under the surface! Furthermore, it is a 'denial mechanism'). Ask a hundred health professionals how they are, and they often cannot answer (they are too busy looking after their patients) so they use 'displacement' as a coping mechanism as well as 'denial' (mothers or managers - in fact anyone with responsibilities - may do the same).

Let's look at why this should be, and how feelings work. On the following page there is an overall map of the journey.

Life's learning cycle

Our life's story is a journey of learning. It unfolds as a series of experiences, each one giving us something else to learn about. It starts when we are born, and continues through childhood into adulthood and ends when we die.

experience = event + emotion (our reaction)
experience = facts + feelings

Our feelings reflect our ever-changing frames of mind as we consider each issue from different points of view. We process an experience by reflecting on it, thinking about it from all angles and perspectives and then we learn from it. In learning we get closure and completion.

This is 'life's' Learning Cycle:

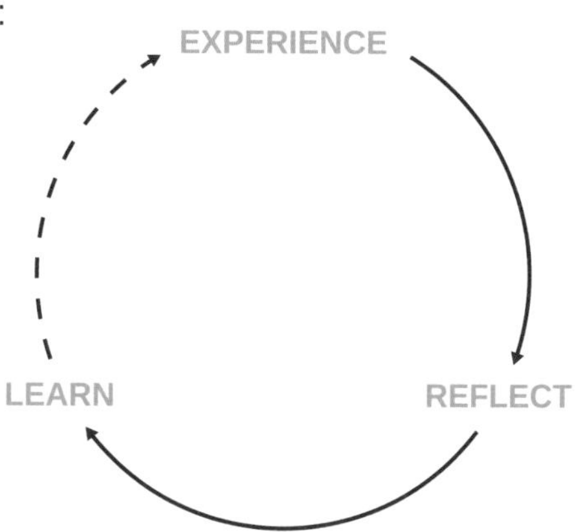

We go round this cycle millions of times in a lifetime. Human beings are successful learners, so the great majority of the time we successfully get round the cycle and add to our 'wisdom' pile.

18.1

Life is a Journey of Learning

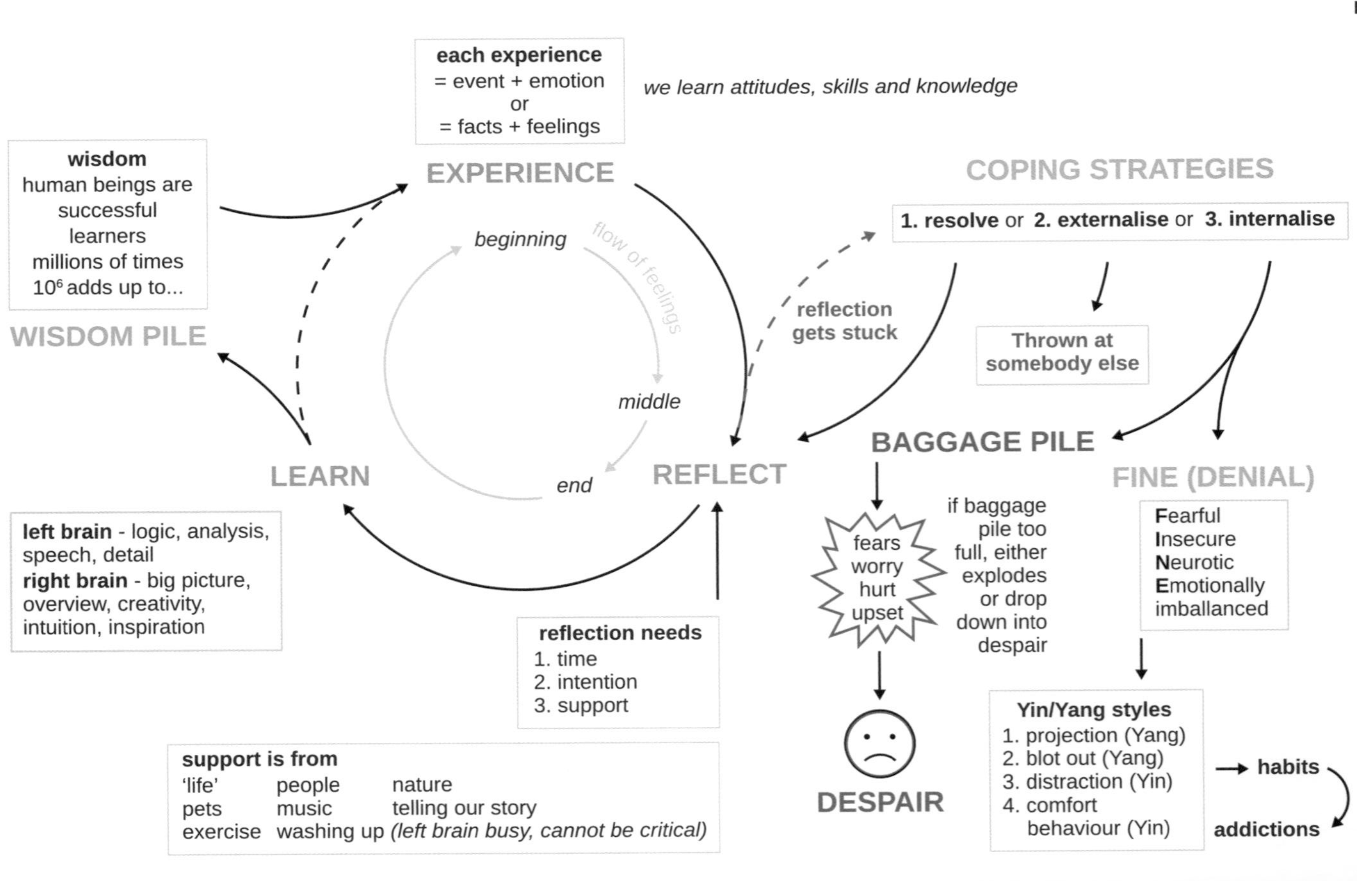

The Wisdom Pile

This contains all our completed experiences and everything we have learned from:

- Personal growth as we continue to mature.
- Relationships with our parents, siblings, family, friends and others we meet.
- The making, maturing and release of attachments.
- The development of knowledge, skills and attitudes to help us perform well.
- Caring and coping skills.

So, what happens if we get stuck?

Every experience starts at the beginning, transits the middle and reaches the end, like any piece of music or story. The events or facts of the story begin, happen and end, no matter what. Feelings usually change effortlessly from moment to moment throughout that story. However, sometimes the flow of feelings can get stuck, often when they are too hot or painful to handle. We feel unsupported, so are unable to deal with them. This happens at the reflection stage - reflection gets stuck.

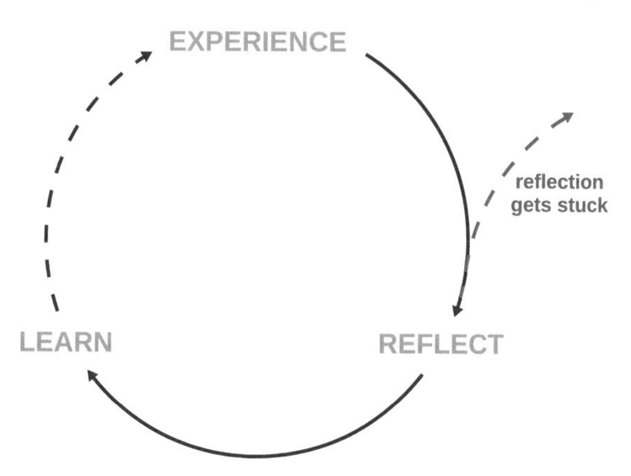

At this point we can do one of three things:

1. We can take ownership of our issues, and get things moving again to a **resolution**.
   Or, we can dissociate and...
2. We can **externalize** them, often at a target.
3. Or we can **internalize** them, burying those feelings deep inside us in our 'baggage' pile.

Hate is hurt projected.

The Baggage Pile

This contains many unresolved issues stuck hidden inside, arising from yesterday, last week, last month, last year, the last relationship, or any time in our lives. Some of this stuff is personal, some family, some tribal, some racial, some gender and some simply because we are humans and thus sentient beings. We file this baggage in our 'anger' file, our 'shame' file, our 'guilt' file, or our files labelled 'me', 'them', 'him', 'her' and so on. We push these files to the back of our minds, telling ourselves we will deal with their contents tomorrow. But, as we know, tomorrow never comes.

So, what happens to this stuff?
Well, the problem is that it is always present in our subconscious in the 'now', and can flip back out to the surface in response to a trigger:

- If you see someone you had an argument with yesterday, the feelings come up again
- If you see someone who looks like the person you had an argument with last week, the feelings come up again
- If you find yourself in a familiar but difficult situation you struggled with last time (with no extra support or training), the feelings come up again

Sometimes the trigger is an anniversary, the same time of year, the same type of person, the same stage of pregnancy or a similar situation.

Once on the surface again, you have an opportunity to re-enter 'life's' Learning Cycle and once again choose to resolve, externalize or internalize the feeling. The bad news is that, without additional support or training, it is likely that the feeling will end up back in the baggage pile, possibly with additional triggers attached to it. The good news is that you can resolve a feeling at any time once you have recognized it (which is often the part that needs the additional training/support to achieve).

So, what happens when the baggage pile gets too full?
In basic terms, it either explodes or we become overwhelmed with it all and start to sink in to sadness or apathy. Or, we use denial (I'm **FINE**), and channel into one of four mechanisms:

- Projection (throwing it all at someone else)
- Blot Out (pretending the issue doesn't exist)
- Distraction (doing something else)
- Comfort Behaviour (soothing ourselves). Sometimes, instead of comfort behaviour, people use control of their own bodies, such as in eating disorders.

Let's consider how we cope with our growing baggage pile in terms of Chinese Cosmology. You may have heard of the age-old principles of Yin and Yang, and be aware of the symbol below.

Yang, the outward, seeking, searching spirit, is considered to be:

- Hot, dry
- Light
- Masculine
- Assertive

Yin, the receptive, knowing, nurturing one, is considered to be:

- Cool, moist
- Dark
- Feminine
- Accepting

Every human is part masculine, part feminine, regardless of what body we wear. Yang protects Yin, and Yin nurtures Yang. Men may sometimes be more masculine (yang), women more feminine (yin), but in reality, we all contain elements of both, hence the spot in the centre of each swirl.

When under pressure, Yin and Yang will display different coping mechanisms:

Yang (externalizes or deletes)	**Yin** (palliates the inner hurt)
projection Throwing the problem at someone/ something else	**distraction** Using many different mechanisms
blot out Using alcohol, illicit substances, devices, screen-time	**comfort behaviour** Classically using food, but there are others

Beware! Coping mechanisms may lead to habits. Habits may become addictions.

Mechanisms

↓

Habits

↓

Addictions

The trouble with defence and coping mechanisms is that they only palliate the underlying issue, and do not reach a healing resolution. As mentioned previously, we get stuck in the reflection phase of 'Life's' Learning Cycle.

Core Feelings of Hurt

Fear
Shame
Sadness
Abandonment
Envy
Loneliness
Indignation
Hatred
Anger

Fear underpins most of these. Fear is countered by love.

PALLIATION does not bring a HEALING RESOLUTION

Stimulus may lead to immediate knee-jerk response, driven by immediate emotion or reflexes. However, we each have 'responsibility' - the ability to choose our response. We can reflect and choose. Remember, the word 'responsibility' can be split in two: **response - ability**. That is, we each have the ability to choose our response at every moment. Taking responsibility can lead to transformation. The following quote is often used to describe the views of Victor Frankl, who survived the concentration camps of the Second War:

"Between stimulus and response there is a space. In that space is our power to choose our response. In our response lies our growth and our freedom."[3]

So, how can we better reflect?

Sometimes reflection is brief and we gain an instant answer. When this doesn't happen there are three things that are necessary to nurture successful reflection.

1. Time and a safe space
2. Intention - we have to want to
3. Support - the key component

Support mechanisms:

- Life - feeling connected to the flow of life. Life itself is coded for success, and we are all part of 'LIFE'.
- Breathing - Regular rhythmic abdominal breathing supports our physiology into coherence and harmony rather than chaos and discord
- Other people - friends, family, professionals
- Telling our story to someone, journaling or written reflection. (What we write in our personal dairy - our inmost thoughts and feelings - does NOT have to be copied to our professional portfolio.)
- Time in nature, or patterns from nature that nurture our software being
- Exercise, walking, playing
- Water - showering or swimming to wash off issues (cold water seems to work better!)
- Music
- Hobbies or activities that give us joy
- Routine tasks (like the washing up!) that engage our left (thinking) brain to allow our right (expressive, creative) brain to consider the issue

These mechanisms allow us to re-live the learning cycle with a positive outcome, resolving the blockage. And so we accept our experience fully, and release any stuck feelings. Another way of dealing with buried issues, with support, follows a similar cycle but observed at a distance to avoid re-experiencing the trauma.

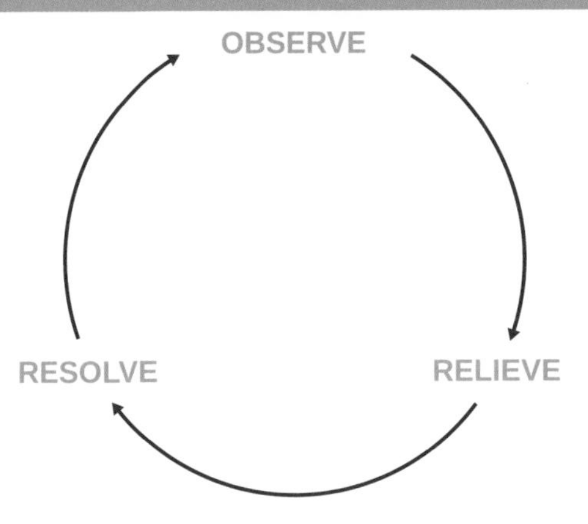

Let's apply this to 'bereavement', a particular case of loss:

Loss, Grief and Bereavement

Loss is the act of losing someone or something. To lose is to be deprived of someone or something, by *"negligence, separation, death or misadventure"*.

Grief is deep sorrow or 'keen regret' - the feeling we may have when we feel the pain of loss. (Pain comes from feeling separate from the support of love). At some level, deep inside, most people feel bereft - though of what they are not quite sure. Perhaps it is a feeling of separation from 'life' itself?

Bereavement is being robbed or deprived of someone or something (such as our health - when we are given bad news), and a subsequent feeling of desolation (loneliness).

So it seems that:

1. We grow an attachment to someone or something (a person, health, a way of life, friends, an income, a job, a place);
2. This attachment has meaning to us, and we have strong feelings about it;
3. We become deprived of the other person or thing, and become separate, through death, accident, or loss;
4. The relationship therefore stops;
5. We feel the loss, and feel sadness, hurt, sorrow, resentment, and so on;
6. The process of feeling the loss is called grieving;
7. The grieving only ends when our feelings are resolved and healed.

Bereavement means losing someone or something (including our health) that we are attached to or love. Loss is painful, especially to our feelings. When we lose someone, we feel the loss:

- of the person,
- of our relationship with them,

- of the hopes, and fears, the joys and the fantasies of this relationship,
- of the shared experiences, the might-have-beens.

In fact - we lose a bit of our self, a part of our meaning structure.

Feelings felt during bereavement			
Hurt	Pain	Shock	Fear
Anger	Numbness	Apathy	Worry
Sadness	Guilt	Resentment	Despair

Yet these feelings, like all feelings, can resolve rather than get stuck. Often they do get stuck - and sometimes stuck for years. 'Flow' is blocked.

When we are bereaved we can feel a turmoil of strong feelings. There is a well-recognised path of progression, though of course we can revisit any phase many times:

Shock
Numbness, Denial
Anger
Distress, Guilt
Bargaining
Sadness, depression
↓ Eventual resolution and reconciliation, acceptance

Accompanying these strong feelings, are thoughts and questions. Actually, we have similar questions every day, but at a time of high emotion, the emotionally laden questions and thoughts seem more significant.

thought	→	resolution
thought + a little emotion	→	partial resolution coloured by emotion
thought + lots of strong emotions	→	turmoil, upset potentially clouded judgement

The two main families of questions we meet are these; the:
- 'What if's, and the:
- 'If only's

We meet these questions every day of the year, because we are thinking, reflective beings - but they are most insistent at times of strong emotions. Each of these questions can be laden with emotion and pain, when we ask them:
- If only I'd been to see her more often
- What if she'd eaten more (vegetables, fruit, sugar)
- If only he hadn't (smoked, driven so fast, been on that road that day)

- What if the doctors had spotted it sooner
- If only they could have saved him
- If only I'd been kinder to him

At a time of high emotion, our judgment may be clouded. With our clouded judgment, we lose our balanced perspective and can resort to blame or guilt, driven by strong feelings.

If we let the 'what if's and 'if only's persist,
They can circle around,
They can then pester us
Unresolved, they fester
Festering, they turn to poison
Which we cast out as blame at someone else
Or hide inside as guilt

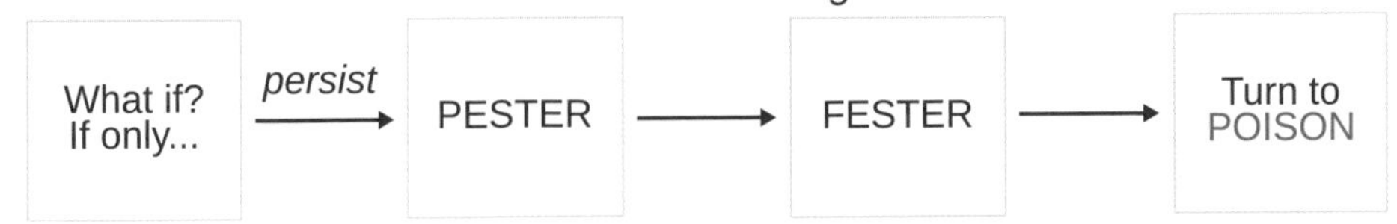

18.2

If the 'what if's and 'if only's are not resolved, or 'put to bed', they persist.

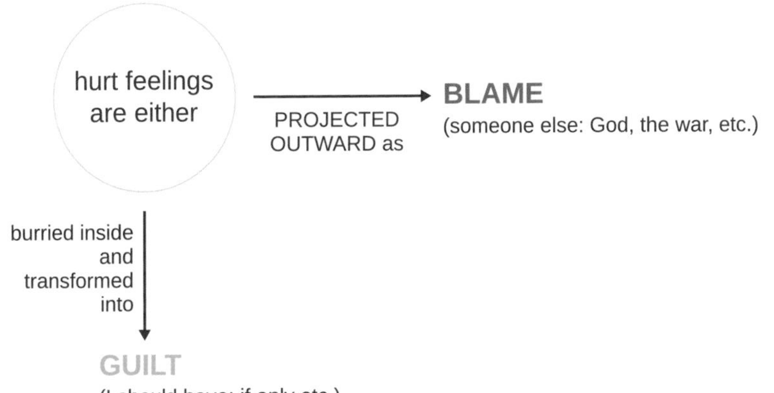

18.3

The poison is then either:

Thrown OUT as Blame - at someone else, or
BURIED INSIDE to fester and to stay as buried hurt.

Of course, neither of these is fair - and both end up hurting ourselves and others - so the challenge is to achieve a healing resolution. So if ever you meet any of these two families, the 'what if's and 'if only's - feel free to tell them to go away!

Turning points and adjusting to change

Emotional Logic explains how we can grow beyond grief by understanding the process. The first step to understanding 'adjusting to change' emotions is to learn the different phases we go through when adjusting, known as 'turning points'. [See section 20 for more explanation and 36 (p179) for diagram].

1. Recognize loss (May be difficulty in recognising loss, or even taking on-board the risk of loss)
2. Prevent loss (A drive to control the situation takes over)
3. Recover loss (we seek to replace the loss or recover our previous position)
4. Let go of loss (we move on, older and wiser)

   It describes the meaning of our reactions to loss and grief as follows. In coping with change, we need to find safety.

Emotion	Means	Useful Purpose
Shock, numbness	'I can't cope'	Stop! Find a safe place to review your resources
Denial	'I can carry on as if nothing has happened'	Put the issue aside for now so I can use my energy for immediate needs
Anger	'I want to prevent the loss of something important to me'	Anger transformed becomes creativity
Guilt	'What if I had done…? Did it cause the loss?'	Learning. Redirected guilt becomes a new perspective of inner choices, and enables us to leave behind the feeling that we might have done something 'wrong'
Bargaining	'What can I do to get back what I've lost?'	We all need energy to take risks to deal with situations in new ways
Sadness, depression	'I feel powerless and empty'	There is only so much one can do - knowing the limits stops me trying for the impossible
Acceptance	Although this loss has happened and I cannot change it, I am still a valued person with a role to play	I can now live life again, as my loved one would wish me to, with more maturity and energy to explore 'life' again

Some of these emotions arise from the urge to change the world out there, others are to change the person inside. You see, shock cuts us off from connection to the 'flow of life'.

When thinking about the useful purpose of shock emotional energy, it needs a safe place to help resolve it. A safe place is a place to go to when you get over the initial shock where you can review your resources and plan your next steps. Your safe place may be:

- A physical place
- A state of mind
- A relationship

It's a useful exercise to think of your own safe places and to ensure they are available to you when needed.

At the bargaining phase, we can move forwards positively. Remember, there are three styles of bargaining, when we are trying to get back something we value that we have lost and still yearn for:

- **Aggressive** I am going to take it, and I don't care what effect that has on you.
- **Passive** I am going to give out subtle messages that I want you to give it to me.
- **Assertive** I can state my need, and hear yours, and between us we can find a way to minimise our losses and maximise our gains.

You can see that of these, only assertive style provides win-win for both parties. In the next chapter, on emotional logic, we will consider this important topic in more detail. With thanks to Alex Aylward, Dr Trevor Griffiths and the Emotional Logic Centre.

Life's Journey - deeper philosophy and into Metaphysics!
(this section is optional reading)
'Life' may start before birth when 'consciousness', individuated into the form of a soul, chooses to incarnate [get into flesh] in a body. In fact, it is an interesting point for society to consider: whether we are human beings having a spiritual experience, or spiritual beings having a human experience.

'Life' takes us on a journey from birth until the present moment. 'Life' continues giving us experiences until our death. Death is when our consciousness finally leaves our physical body. Our bodies [our vehicles] then stop working and decay.

'Life' brings us events. 'Life' invites us to participate, and usually to say 'yes'. These events give us rich sensory experiences, every moment of our day and night. We process these as electrical and electronic information signals. 'Life' brings us situations and relationships for us to experience. In experiencing them we can be enriched, inspired, uplifted, and we can learn; this is '**flow**'. We can also have negative or positive reactions, and learn - or we can fail to learn. This can become '**blockage**', if we hold onto our inner reaction without 'relaxing' and 'releasing'.

We handle this information by processing the experiences through our software energy system. Experiences 'flow' through us. We process the vast majority of data that arises from the experiences effortlessly (smooth). Sometimes the event sets up disturbance in our mind and body (negative or positive). If this disturbance persists, it can give rise to a blockage: we hold onto an emotional picture or representation of the event. Subjectively, this is now an unresolved, incomplete experience, which will continue to cycle around in our energy system until resolved. This is a jangly, jarring, discordant state, which we often retain and bury in our subconscious. Indian tradition calls this a "samskara"; an energy pattern that we cling to, and have not yet released. This cycling is below the level of our conscious mind, but can be triggered back to consciousness by a similar event - in fact by anything that resonates such as a sight, sound, smell, look, experience.[4]

We cannot choose what 'life' brings to us but we ***can*** choose how we react.

The natural order is to Experience, Reflect, Learn and Release. We are always experiencing and releasing. ERLRG, Experience, Reflect, Learn and Release, with Gratitude. However, if we hold onto an experience - whether nice or nasty; giving us pleasure or pain - then we cling to and retain the energy disturbance associated with the memory.

We process experiences through our energy system and especially through an open heart; through the heart chakra [Chakra is Sanskrit for 'spinning wheel'; a vortex of invisible energy]. Any experience that leaves a disturbance leaves a jangly discordant pattern that sticks in our energy system (a bit like 'bad areas' on the hard disk of a computer). These disturbances are either in the chakra system, the meridians, or in other energy patterns.

With every experience, we need to relax and release. Smoothly, from Inner Stillness. Enjoy, accept, relax, release. When our hearts and minds are open, then there is '**flow**'. When there is disturbance, our hearts and minds may close, and we get '**blockage**'. Open heart and mind means experiences move through us, they are processed, and 'life' is enriched which leads to smooth 'flow'. Resistance brings stiffening and a partial closure of heart and mind. Therefore, we retain the incomplete unresolved samskara and cause it to cycle around in our energy system, costing us energy to keep it there. This is a 'jangly blockage'. What We Resist, Persists. WWRP

If we accept reality and stop resisting it; if we relax and allow 'flow', then things improve, 'life' flows smoothly and problems become projects. Stressful situations become growth opportunities and we move forwards on our journey of growth and our spiritual journey as beings of mind, body and spirit.

Choose to relax and release, choose joy over pleasure, choose to accept and release, choose to accept and be content. Smile and the world smiles with you; be unhappy and you are miserable alone. 'Life' is a mirror that reflects back to us our thoughts and fears, so choose your thoughts wisely! The Law of Attraction says that What You Give Out Is What You Get Back - WYGOIWYGB! In relaxing and releasing, we learn forgiveness, which is beneficial to ourselves, as we will see below.

Conscious Reflection in more detail

Reflection is the key process that helps us gain meaning in 'life' and re-view our experiences. It helps us look at them again, reframe them and see what is true and what is good in them. Reflection helps us give meaning to and to gain closure on each of our life's experiences. Reflection brings us insight, wisdom, perspective and a detached overview. We have to take time to do this, we have to wish to, and we have to accept support. 'Life', however, gives us choices: we do not have the choice as to whether we accept and process all of life's experiences - we have to do this as a matter of course. However, we do have a choice as to how we process them - consciously and with support, or using one of the four mechanisms of projection, blot out, distraction or comfort behaviour to provide temporary palliation, thus avoiding the issue. However, the issue will always catch up with us and so we will always have to process our samskaras in one way or another. Ideally we do this without accumulating so much burden that our 'life force' is handicapped and we may drift into patterns of emotional imbalance, go 'out of tune' and may be even become ill.

Often we get caught up in the trivia of events, caught in a web of emotions, or trapped in our own or someone else's Drama Triangle. At this point, the 'flow of life' gets stuck and reflection ceases. Reflection gets stuck in the tension of suspension, awaiting resolution. We need to get Reflection moving again. What things can we do to find support? Well, breathing is very important. We need to slow down our breathing from the anxious fast shallow upper chest breathing of stress, to the deep slow abdominal breathing of relaxation. Slow deep breaths through the nose right down into the abdomen, and slowly out again. Counting slowly to ten can help us rebalance too. By inspiring (breathing in), we can reconnect ourselves with the flow of 'life' that supports us at all times. When we are still within, we can listen to the still small voice of calm that connects us to the flow of 'life'. There is a whole science of yogic breathing to help us!

When we feel supported, we connect to a specific deeper pattern of harmony that allows us to be still and process our experiences to completion.

Keeping a journal or diary, or notes on our phone of positive reflection can be powerful. If you take time to reflect at the end of the day and write down 5 positive reflections, by the end of the month you will have 150 positive deposits in the account! Spending time in nature, receiving kind care and attention, listening to music that soothes or inspires us or connecting to other supportive harmonious patterns of information can help us retune. Such patterns include Bach and other flower essences, and other informational (non-chemical) approaches.

Forgiveness

One key thing that can happen during this process is forgiveness. Forgiveness (the releasing or pardoning of a debt owed to you) is magical and transformational. It involves the release of an attachment we have constructed in our minds. 'To err is human, to forgive is divine'[5]. As we experience, as we relax and release, we often take a personal perspective and become intimately attached to the experience. In order to release this attachment, we may have to:

- **Take part in the experience**
- **Love the experience**
- **Forgive aspects of the experience**
- **Release and move on**

So with any issue, we have to accept that it has happened, and acknowledge it in all its aspects. Then (this is the big one!) we have to forgive in three ways. First we have to forgive the other person, then the event – and (often a huge step) we then have to forgive ourselves, for the part we played and for how we acted. In forgiving, we release judgments and feelings that act as blocks to healing. In doing so we reclaim our power that we locked away in these judgments and allow ourselves back into the flow of 'life', remembering, and re-membering (putting ourselves back together again with the bits we lost when we tied them up in the issue that was stuck).

This process helps us release the blocked issue, the samskara, and then move on in life. The one person that 'forgiveness' helps most is ourselves. We release the hurts and grudges and our inner neurochemistry changes accordingly to a more healthy state. Acknowledge, forgive, release, move on.

Reflection gives us perspective, a bigger view, and (sometimes) enables us to see the full picture. It helps us unlearn patterns of restriction and can help us transcend our own and society's cultural group-think.

Peter's Cosmic Zoom - perhaps the ultimate perspective?

One evening, I was talking to two friends, both called Peter. Separately they described how they deal with difficult situations, and how they achieve an overview.

It ran something like this :

- Just imagine yourself in the room, but outside yourself watching the issue.
- Next imagine yourself observing from above, looking down on the issue.
- Now imagine you are several hundred feet above, looking down.
- Next distance yourself further again, so you are looking down at the issue from miles above.
- Finally, look down from outer space, and see how important the issue really is!

  Now *that's* Perspective!

Without perspective, the prison walls of narrow thinking, (especially if governed by negative emotions such as fear, worry, hurt, hate, anger and others) trap our thinking and stop us seeing the bigger picture

Ego's Prison Walls of Narrow Thinking Stop Us Seeing the Bigger Picture

Yet, in 'life', we often take things personally and so have difficulty in releasing, because we may find ourselves in states of anger or guilt. But it is in 'forgiveness' that we release toxic patterns of negative thinking and feeling. By holding onto them, we only hurt ourselves, as we hold on to samskaras and as a result neurotransmitters of stress and tension continue to circle round our bodies. Healing and releasing samskaras frees up energy and vitality and contributes powerfully to our health.

Many have thought about this over the ages - after all, are we human beings aspiring to a spiritual experience, or spiritual beings having a human experience?

Some suggestions from Ancient Wisdom, about the 'Game of Life':

1. The purpose of 'life' is to gain wisdom, experience of 'life's' situations and to learn to love, whatever the circumstances or hardship. Our emotions are constantly with us, so part of the purpose is to accept and understand those emotions.
2. We choose to meet with a group of souls to share experiences to mutual benefit and gain. Not all experiences are pleasant - but we tend not to learn much by always having an easy time. All experiences are, however, opportunities to learn.
3. We attract to ourselves through the great 'universal law of attraction' (resonance) whatever we consciously or subconsciously think about, be it

pleasant or unpleasant, positive or negative. We also attract experiences through which we may learn, and so gain wisdom.
4. However, because nobody ever told us the rules of the game of 'life', we tend to keep mucking it up unless we are lucky.
5. Nobody ultimately judges us more accurately than we do ourselves.

Dr Edward Bach was the gifted intuitive developer of Bach Flower Remedies that help us retune aspects of our being and psyche that have gone out of balance. He thought deeply about our emotions, and what factors could keep us healthy. He also formulated a philosophy about the journey of life in a paper called 'Free Thyself'.[6] His thinking runs something like this:

1. Health is harmony of mind, body and spirit. We should aim to live with an open heart, free from cares and worries.
2. Every person needs a purpose, a reason for living.
3. Each person is a small part of consciousness, or 'life', or the great spirit, on a journey on earth. (Certainly we are all part of a two billion year process of evolution of life forms on our planet, and 'life' is designed to be successful).
4. This journey on earth is here to be enjoyed to the full, whatever work we do.
5. There is always divine help for us at all times on the journey, especially if we stray from our path.
6. Our souls will guide us in every circumstance and every difficulty if only we 'still' ourselves and listen to the little voice within.
7. When guided by our souls to follow our path we radiate happiness and perfect health.
8. The journey of 'life' is one of experiences and challenges, the purpose of which is to gain wisdom.

If we wish to believe in some of these concepts, it is easier to feel supported in 'life', to feel connected to something rather greater than just human life, to feel part of all that is. It is when we feel supported and part of a greater plan that we feel connected. Connected, perhaps, to 'life', or to whatever we each conceive the god-force to be.

The Enlightened Gardener by Sydney Banks.[7]

In this allegorical tale, Sydney Banks proposes that "'life' is an illusionary, spiritual journey confined within the boundaries of time, space and matter". He states there are three spiritual gifts, which are:

- The power and the gift of Universal Mind, (the source of all intelligence and energy of 'life').
- The power and the gift of Universal Consciousness (which allows us to be aware of our existence) and
- The power and the gift of Universal Thought (Which guides us through the world in which we live as free-thinking agents).

He says "Wherever you go, Truth is with you always", and that all of our problems arise from our own individual thoughts. Other memorable points he suggests are that "Universal Thought is the mystical paint brush, your creative agent, and the reality you survey is the picture it creates".

Come let it be today.

Come let it be today, that we sow the seeds of our tomorrows,
And make our visions come and live in purest joy, and banish all our sorrows.
Come now and truly be engaged in life's own seeking for simplicity
Before the flower, first the seed
Before the love, first the need
To give unceasingly to 'life', as the River flows to the Sea, his wife

Ken Dryden

Perhaps our challenge is to surrender to 'life' as a flow and allow 'consciousness' to flow through our human vessel - truly "Thy Will, not my will" - which gives us all the chance of raising our conscious level above selfish ego choices.

Fear and Insecurity - Blockages to Flow

At times we feel insecure, frightened or worried. This insecurity comes from fear: fear of change, fear of being different, fear of being alone, fear of being wrong, fear of being unsupported and of course fear of death. However, we are not actually separate little egos in selfish 'little me' worlds; we are each individual parts of a much greater whole, connected by 'synchronicity' and 'connectedness'. We are part of a world wide web of consciousness, of which we are all little parts. The mystery of 'life' plays out as millions of 'my story's'. The thoughts of Banks, Ken Wilber, Tim Freke and others give us the possibility of appreciating that we live life from inside out, not from outside in. When we allow ourselves a bigger perspective - a cosmic zoom - we allow ourselves to see 'flow' again; to notice how fear is small and acts to block our progress.

Synchronicity was popularised by Jung, whilst modern physics shows us the interconnectedness of all things. Some might say "Coincidence is God's way of remaining anonymous" - but a friend put it like this: "'life' is driven by coincidence - it is the coinciding of patterns of potential that brings some of them into existence".

Mindful Self Compassion is an approach of kindness towards self, which helps us dissolve our fears and worries by lovingly holding our 'selves' in an attitude of compassion and kindness. This can be very powerful for our own health and well-being.

Perhaps one final taboo for many is to discuss death. It may be inevitable, but many of us would like to pretend that we are invincible and immortal and avoid thinking about the issue. We are often too busy! Dr Penny Sartori PhD, a nurse working in intensive care, writes clearly about the subject in The Wisdom of Near Death Experiences[9] and brings us interesting conclusions from her prospective five year study; a piece of scientific research it is difficult to argue with. Raymond Moody's Life after Life[8] is also useful, as is the Tibetan Book of the Dead[10]. The following are some personal thoughts on the topic, feel free to ignore or dismiss them if you wish.

Death and Dying

Death is when we stop using our body as the vehicle for our consciousness. Death is when 'Consciousness', working through the i, stops using the body, and receives back that i into the greater whole (the little i back into the big I).

Death is not when we are separated from life, but when we are freed of the restriction of one single life incarnated on earth - when we become whole with 'life' again. Of course - we were never separate - except in believing that we were!

Traditionally around the twentieth century, two thirds of the world believed in reincarnation; one third not. These proportions may now have changed.

So which is right? Well, just to develop what we discussed just now, some think that:

- We come into life on earth, in a human body, as a stream of consciousness, and use that body for a lifetime.
- That we bring in skills and talents to help us, which can be developed further (Mozart brought in one tremendous skills package to be writing concertos by the age of seven. Some children seem to be 'old souls' or to have unexpected skills such as carefully turning over the pages of a paper book aged 15months - when many children just tear cardboard!)
- That we bring in issues to resolve (often with people, this may be with past places and circumstances).
- That we may have a broad outline plan of our lives (a 'life plan') which we can choose to follow (or not).
- That the stage set of our 'life', with the actors of family, friends and strangers is where we work out these issues.
- That some of the issues feel intensely personal, or familiar (but may be just projections from our own perspective).
- That we may come in with a 'soul group' that supports each other.
- That some of the issues are archetypal.
- That we grow from resolving these issues and from using our gifts wisely.
- that 'life' and 'consciousness' is enriched by all our experiences - every single one of them!

Many believe in the whole wonder of ‘life’, of our oneness with ‘consciousness’. In fact, some recent thinking from physics[12] points to a conclusion that ‘consciousness’ informs/relates to ‘information’, which relates to ‘energy’, which is interchangeable with ‘matter’. $E=mC^2$

Dying is something to be accepted and expected (when we’ve finished garnering experiences!). Dying is the moving over from one ‘plane’ to another.

The biggest problems about death and dying are fear and ignorance. The ego fears:

1. the Annihilation of the ego
2. Pain
3. Loss of its attachments and meaning structure

Yet if we view life as a journey, things can be different.

A journey in which a soul incarnates into a body for a lifetime, with of course:

- A beginning
- A middle
- And an end

A journey when an ‘aspect of consciousness’, of the ‘great I’, chooses to come to earth as a little ‘i’. At the end of the journey, the little ‘i' returns, with all its wonderful experiences, back into the big I. At our death, our ‘soul’ (which used the body as a vehicle) passes over to the ‘other side’.

When we ‘pass over’, our ‘consciousness’ leaves the physical plane.

People who have had near death experiences often describe a tunnel and then a arm, golden light; a loving light at the far end. This is the journey of the soul returning to spirit.

Those with near-death experiences (i.e. they ‘came back’) often say that they had a knowing, or were told, that it was not yet time to return to the ‘light’. So they came back to the earth plane and brought their consciousness back into their body.

We are always welcomed back at 'death'; back into ‘consciousness’ itself, often by a warm light. Welcomed by those who have loved us or who do love us. And there is usually someone we recognize. There are also many invisible guides and helpers to aid this process. In fact, we are always welcomed if we allow ourselves to be and we will always move over smoothly, if we allow ourselves to. Furthermore, we are often welcomed personally, by those who have known and loved us before; perhaps as parents, grandparents, or other friends who have died before us - according to what we believe. When we go, we are governed by our belief system - so if we believe in a smooth transition and ‘heaven’ beyond - we will find it, as we return to and mingle with, ‘consciousness’.

We may then undergo a “life’ review’, when all of life is viewed and reviewed. It’s thought that people review all of ‘life’ in a positive light, looking for the learning, and that one key thing they value is the quality of relationships, the love they have shown and the wisdom they have learned - not how much money they have earned!

But the beliefs and thinking we held during our lifetime can trap us.

A lot of people either haven’t thought about what happens after death, or choose to believe that there is nothing. If we believe strongly in no life after death, or we believe only in the earth plane, these beliefs may cause some difficulties.

Or, if our body dies very rapidly or violently, we may be so shocked that we get stuck ‘in limbo’. So, we can be held ‘in limbo’ - between the one world (earth plane) and the next (spirit world) by our own belief or by shock. If so, these beliefs may trap us and prevent us from ‘moving on’ - although the light and the ‘welcome’ are always there for us.

But every soul has freedom to choose - so if you choose to believe in nothing - then that will dictate your experiences, according to the ‘laws of attraction’ and that Energy Follows Thought. But you can always choose again! Remember, choices have consequences!

So it’s useful for people to know about the following process. Both for themselves, and to help others. This way every time we close our eyes, we can relax (as we do when we go to sleep every night), know we will be looked after, and can look for the light when it is time to die.

‘Looking for the light’ is really important. The light may be bright, it may be so intense that it is unexpected, but it is always there, awaiting us, ready to welcome us back and to add all our personal experiences to the wisdom of the world.

So it can be useful to help people in their last days by reminding them:

“One day, we all pass over. We stop using our bodies, and move over into the realm of spirit, of pure consciousness. When we go, it’s just like going to sleep - but we are welcomed. Each time you close your eyes, let yourself ‘Look for the light’, and, one day, you will see somewhere around you a very bright light. At the same time, or before, you may meet some family, grandparents, parents, brothers or sisters who have died before. They will welcome you and will look after you. Be confident, and know that all will be well. You will be looked after, supported and guided at every moment, as you move back toward the Light”.

A learning area for us all…

Conclusion

We hope these writings may help illuminate some areas of life that are often hidden and provide you with some guidance through areas that often cause us difficulties. Michael Roads gives some guidance in the following:

“I would like to offer the way out of fear. Trust! Trust in ‘self’. Trust that despite all possible evidence to the contrary, you are both adequate and capable. Trust that the immortal ‘being’ you truly are has the intelligence to deal with anything that comes into your life. After all, you are the author of the book of your life! Trust that you truly are a magnificent, metaphysical, multidimensional ‘being of love and light’. This is your ‘truth’. Trust it.

“In all life there is ‘spirit’. You are a spiritual ‘being’. The soul whom you are is the growth of the individualisation of spirit. In every moment of your life you are expressing spirit... and all spirit is ‘one’. Spiritually, you are ‘one’ with all life, with every person. Positively accepting or negatively critical, the way you think is the way you will treat yourself and other people and it is the way you will create for ‘life’ to deal with you. Every life form in ‘nature’ is an expression of spirit, the same spirit that expresses in you.

“Through spirit you are connected to everything. Nothing is outside Self, for Self is a boundless and measureless expression of spirit. When soul withdraws from the body, spirit remains with soul, for just as soul is an expression of spirit, so is body an expression of soul. Spirit cannot die, ‘life’ cannot die. All that happens at so-called human death is that consciousness/spirit/soul withdraws from the physical body, continuing as a metaphysical Being of Love and Light on a non-physical level of expression. You are an eternal Being of Love with the freedom to express Self in whatever way you care to imagine. Your imagination is creation; whatever you continually imagine you will eventually experience. Be careful with your imagination. All that you constantly imagine will invariably be part of your ‘life’. You are a creator. Imagine yourself as a Being of Love and Light. That's wisdom!

“In Love and Light ...”

Michael J. Roads[11]

We are all Creators. Imagination enables us to channel ‘universal thought’. *“If you can dream it, you can do it.”*

“If not me, then who? If not now, then when?”

Final Thoughts: How Can You Improve Your Emotional Intelligence?
Compiled by Dr Shankar Kamath

1. Take responsibility for your emotions and your happiness.
2. Examine your own feelings rather than the actions or motives of other people.
3. Develop constructive coping skills for specific moods. Learn to relax when your emotions are running high and to get up and move when you are feeling down.
4. Make hunting for the silver lining a game. Look for the humour or life lesson in a negative situation.
5. Be honest with yourself. Acknowledge your negative feelings, look for their source, and come up with a way to solve the underlying problem.
6. Show respect by respecting other people's feelings.
7. Avoid people who invalidate you or don't respect your feelings.
8. Listen twice as much as you speak.
9. Pay attention to non-verbal communication. We communicate with our whole selves. Watch faces, listen to tone of voice, and take note of body language.
10. Realize that improving your emotional intelligence will take time and patience.

Notes
WYGOIWYGB The Law of Attraction says that what you give out is what you get back.
ERL Experience, Reflect, Learn
ERLRG Experience, Reflect, Learn and Release, with Gratitude.
WWRP What We Resist, Persists

Reflection points:
- What is the difference between ‘Smooth’ and ‘Jangly’?
- What is the difference between ‘Flow’ and ‘Blockage’?
- How do you reflect? What helps you?
- What events or experiences has this section made you think about?
- How do you find perspective in ‘life’?
- What happens if you ask yourself this question from a point of inner stillness: ‘what is it that I now know that I need to do next?’
- What might you choose to change in your ‘life’?
- Would it help to keep a journal or special place to record positive reflections?
- Do you have a philosophy of ‘life’?
- Which of the concepts above resonate with you?
- Do any of them cause you tension or irritation? Can you work out why?

Asking the ‘whys’ makes you wise.

Emotional Chaos Theory

A variable amount of stress can stimulate the immune system and brain, especially when the capacity remains for personal responsiveness, choice, and hope to achieve goals. Harm may start for the body's physiology and the brain's neurochemistry, however, when stress becomes unrelenting, or when no achievements allow variability and congratulation. Booking up short breaks from work in advance - and taking them - is a sensible strategy to manage a heavy workload. It is the variability that counts, not just the relaxation.

Thus says the chaos theory approach to well-being. A change is as good as a rest. We all need routines to stay healthy; and we all need to break them every now and again. We need to breathe in and to breathe out regularly, and occasionally to have a sigh or a yawn, or a sundowner sip.

Mathematicians who have developed 'chaos theory' since the 1980's become profoundly irritated when people like me apply their rarefied theories to the real world, and demonstrate that improved well-being does indeed follow when people choose to act in accordance with chaos theory principles that bring about 'emergent order'. In any physical system, the same 'simple rules' of emergent self-organisation apply at any and every hierarchical level of 'system', from weather forecasting, to the biochemistry of a single body, to family social dynamics, to inter-cultural conflict in troubled areas of the world.[1] Identifying these simple rules of self-organisation is not the same as blindly imposing artificial order by obeying external laws that govern only behaviour, even though 'advice' about diet and exercise may have good evidence.

This chapter on emotional self-care will use words and diagrams to explain the simple rules of emotional self-organisation that the purist mathematicians can only say with symbols and equations. I shall be describing in simple terms how to apply the new 'Emotional Chaos Theory' approach to well-being to personal and professional development.[2] At the start, however, I need to say that, irritatingly, 'Chaos Theory' has been mis-named. It ought to be called 'The-emergence-of-order-out-of-chaos-by-feedback… Theory', but that's not a good sound bite. It is nevertheless true. The question we shall address here is, what sort of feedback can turn an *emotional system* that is in turmoil or overload into a responsive, adaptive social system, and one that generates improved personal identity with empathic effectiveness to influence change?

Emotional Logic

Every one of us has heard stories of people who say something like, "That was a terrible time to go through, and I wouldn't wish it on anyone else, but I have come out stronger for it." Emotional Logic was developed by a doctor in the 1990's as a *lifelong learning* variant of systemic family therapy that accelerates 'coming out stronger'.[3] It uses lifelong learning *feedback principles* from chaos theory to help people explore and find a sensible path through changing situations, which empowers them to take some reasonable risks that build relationships.

The exploratory nature of the learning makes this a *personal development* alternative to therapeutic counselling or medication. Finding the path prevents common mental illnesses, and reduces socially disruptive behaviour, by improving emotional insight and empathic understanding. It also improves the capacity to make better decisions. Choosing to apply Emotional Logic early accelerates the emergence of order out of chaos, both internally and socially.

For millennia, from the ancient Greek Stoics onwards, there has been a philosophical 'strain of thought' running through educated society that emotion gets in the way of pure reason, and should be expunged from humanity. But in this third Millennium CE, using advanced neuroscience technology, the opposite has been shown to be true by the award-winning neuroscientist Antonio Damasio.[4] He found that emotion is essential for the human capacity to make choices between equally reasonable options for behaviour. Without emotion to 'weight' the options for values-based thriving, the human being's capacity to socially function gets paralysed. Emotional Logic makes that truth active, getting movement back into life when life feels stuck. Pure reason, neuroscience tells us, truly is limited to armchairs.

The 'Life Cycle Diagram'

Emotions properly understood can enable people to walk this sometimes-uncomfortable truth about reasoned risk-taking constructively. When stress accumulates, the walk goes around the 'Life Cycle' diagram shown here.

I have been surprised at how many people have never connected the unpleasant range of emotions that we call 'grieving' with love, in it's widest sense of 'creative connection to someone or something valued'. To the majority of people, feelings of anxiety, fear, brittleness, anger, guilt, yearning, emptiness and sadness seem to come from nowhere, as if just to spoil life, or as punishment, or as a sign of some weakness or failure or illness. But grief emotions, whether starting from bereavement or accumulating from small daily disappointments and setbacks, are in-built genetically into our *survival kit*. They impel us to move in unusual ways to adjust when change has pushed us out of a comfort zone. Grief has a purpose. It is the price we pay for loving, the uneven path we have to walk to explore how to re-connect with people in new ways during times of change, thus to restore the joy of love.

You only grieve if you have loved; this honours you and others as human beings

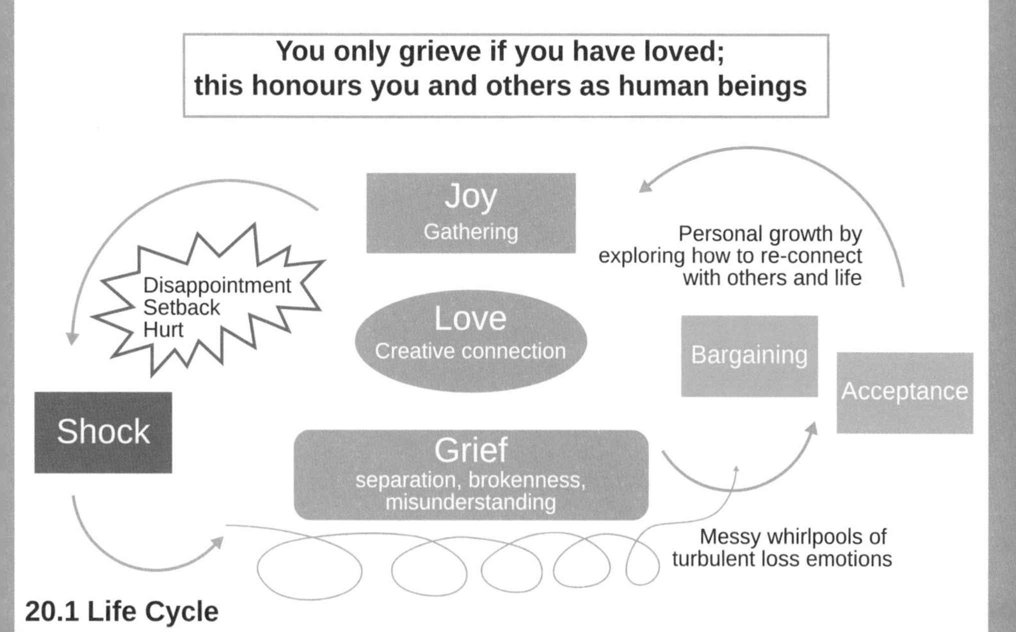

20.1 Life Cycle

The life cycle shown here revolves around that human fundamental of dynamic connection between two or more people who are different to each other. Anyone who has taken part in team-building exercises knows that there must be diversity in groups for the most creative solutions to emerge in problem situations. Diversity is vital for renewed life and the thriving of new beginnings.

A joy can grow when people cooperate effectively. Many people like to imagine love to be that cotton-wool cuddly joy, but wherever there is diversity there will at some point always be some disagreement, disappointment or misunderstanding. “Why are you not doing what I expected? What is wrong with you? Or, what is wrong with me!” When people doubt their resources to manage separation or brokenness or misunderstanding, the joy of love can crumble into Shock, with feelings of anxiety, fear, panic, or being stunned and numb. Love has turned to grief, but it is still love. Love turned to grief has the same purpose, to build creative connection with others - it is just that now the emotions are unpleasant - for good reasons.

Grief is a collection of several unpleasant emotions, not one emotion alongside others. Grieving or mourning (what we do as we grieve) is a process that moves us in unusual ways to explore how to re-connect when change has pushed us out of a comfort zone. This uncomfortable, even painful process, is helped by understanding how these unpleasant emotions are parts of a single process of *adjustment*. However, the unpleasantness of it means that many people get stuck here, trying to get rid of the feelings and unable to see how ultimately their purpose is to move and restore re-connection with others, so that the joy of love may be reappear.

The right-hand corner of the life cycle diagram

Within that emotional grieving process there are two 'preparation states' that we call 'growth points', where people self-organise to explore some new way through the situation - Bargaining (to recover) and Acceptance (to let go of) a single named loss in a situation. More could be said about these personal growth points, but for now I want to say that this right-hand corner of the life cycle diagram is where Emotional Logic differs from mindful emotional regulation. Becoming mindful of emotions is part of Shock turning to its useful purpose (to think more clearly in a safe place), but the growth points empower people then to move on from their safe places constructively, to take some reasonable risks in life to restore relationship and discover new beginnings that restore some shared joy to life.

Emotional Stepping Stones

Emotional Logic develops the work of Kavanaugh and later the British hospice movement into the areas of mental health promotion and personal development. It applies a renewed understanding of seven core emotional states in the adjustments of bereavement (not five 'stages' of Kübler-Ross), to the effects of multiple small loss reactions accumulating for everyday disappointments, setbacks and hurts. This set of core emotions work together as one process of adjustment to loss or potential loss. Several losses can occur within one disappointment, however, for example failing an exam can bring the loss of self-respect, hope, career, money, time, friendships, etc. People can be angry about one loss, guilty about another, shocked about a third and depressed about the future, all at the same time. Then each emotion cannot fulfil its useful purpose to help adjustments in social settings. Tension, distress and confusion may build up inside instead.

Emotional Logic slows down and spreads out this overwhelming emotional turmoil to the point where reason and emotion can come into a partnership to energise a sensible way forward with others. It uses the imagery of crossing a river (or swamp) to explain the useful purposes of emotional preparations. These preparation states are called 'emotional Stepping Stones' for adjustment. They are firm 'inner places', where an active balance of thoughts, physical re-organisation, social messaging in the wider context are brought together as a balance ready to make the next adjustment step or leap. The names of these seven core states we write with capital letters, to emphasise that they are more than mere fleeting feelings of emotion - Shock, Denial, Anger, Guilt, Bargaining, Depression (not clinical depression), and Acceptance.

The 'Turning Points' diagram shown below expands the bottom half of the life cycle diagram. The four arrows across the top are the Logic of adjustment. The *process* of adjusting to the losses hidden within any change or disappointment (un-named because there are too many, usually) can be logical. We can make decisions about where we want to be in it. We can 'turn to face the situation' in any of these frames of mind (recognise loss, prevent it, recover it, let go of it). Bargaining is what we do to influence situations to recover a loss; but if that fails a growing sense of my limits and powerlessness may appear, with a depressive emptiness that is not a clinical depression, but a barren place of decision 'where to go next'. Either go back to try some different way of Bargaining, or go on by choosing to let go of what had previously been so valued a part of life. There is often no right or wrong decision. Depressive emptiness is where we learn to grow in wisdom.

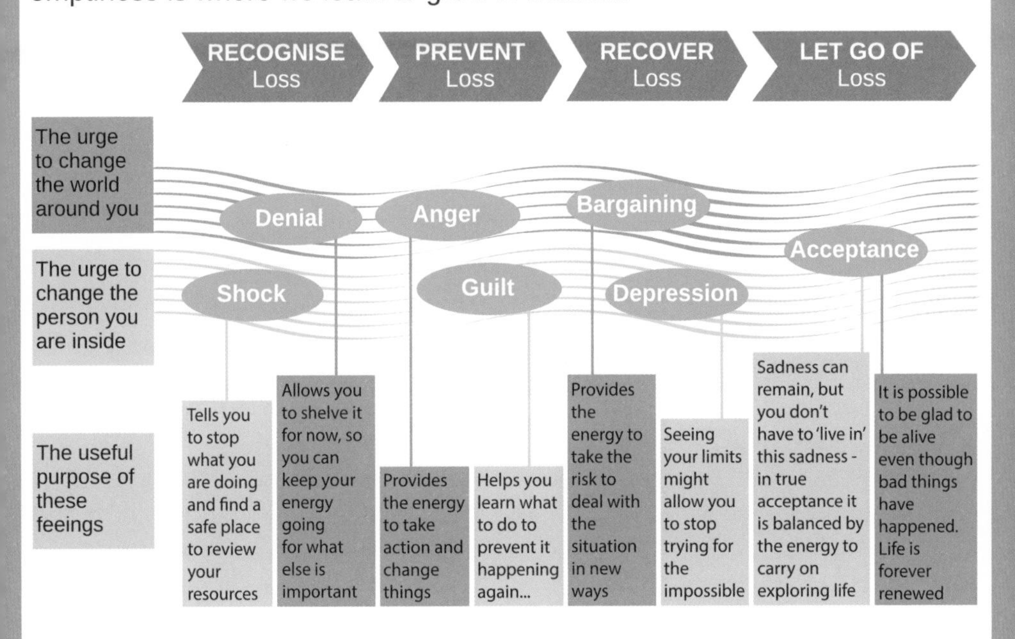

20.2 Turning Points as you adjust to change

But... people tend to go through this process not in a logical way. Although loss emotions are vital as our personal energy self-organising to make the adjustments, the fact that they feel unpleasant is often distracting. At each Turning Point there is a pair of emotional preparations, directed either outwards as an urge to change the world, or inwards as an urge to change the person you are inside. Rather than understanding them as messages to take 'time out' in a safe place to name and plan how to use these emotions to manage the potential losses that are driving them, we easily knee-jerk react, and never slow down to recognise what is really important in this situation. In so doing we may slip off the firm emotional Stepping Stones as we lose balance, and get a bootful of water instead in shallow whirlpools of emotions where the flow of life diverts around the firm places to balance. We get lost in the feelings, and lose the sense of purpose that might otherwise be built by naming the underlying personal values.

Learning to apply the Turning Points diagram in emotional situations *is* the consistent feedback needed to restore emotional order to the adjustment process from chaos. This diagram summarises the simple rules of connection between core unpleasant emotions, which enable people to choose how to move on in a creative direction to adjust constructively with others through the growth points.

Emotional preparations include a facial expression, body language, para-verbal language (voice volume, tone and pacing), and pheromone chemicals released in perspiration. Your emotions thus alert others to potentially vital changes for relationship survival, and theirs are alerting you at subtle levels continuously. Emotion is *social physiology*. The purpose of unpleasant emotion is to connect people into shared movement to adjust together in difficult situations.

However, we complex human beings can *re-activate* these preparations states when recalling memories. When individuals ruminate on problems, the subtle emotional re-activations can *disrupt* the spontaneity, and the clarity, of social information-sharing 'in the present'. People can become lost in a world of "What if's?" and "If only's?". This adds social confusion, separation and relational brokenness to situations as others fail to make sense of the social messages that disturbed people are giving out. The resulting social chaos reflects externally in the world the inner confusion, separations and brokenness that people may feel.

Restoring movement to life when people feel stuck

Recognising when stress is becoming unrelenting is the starting place for health. Emotional Logic gets inside that feeling of stuckness, or treadmill, or overload, by using 'tools' (card-sorting and worksheets) that map the emotional chaos within. The patterns of emotion thus seen, into which the logical sequence of the 'Turning Point' diagram has curled inside you, guide where the feedback learning could untangle emotions, and release the trapped personal energy with which you could start to influence your way out.

Restored emotional order, which is a physiological *dynamic*, rapidly can settle sleep patterns, restore social well-being, and improve physical health. The capacity to make choices of diet and exercise improves, so that health is less of an external demand, and more an emergent lifestyle from within. Energy is more available for adaptability, so that a change does truly become as good as a rest.

Whirlpools of loss emotions

Imagine the facial expression and body posture that would let someone else know that you are angry. Try doing it now just for a second, when no-one is looking. Now imagine the facial expression and body posture that would let someone else know you are shocked. Do it quickly! Now… do both of those at the same time…

You can't, I know! You have just experienced a 'whirlpool of loss emotions'. Neither can properly prepare your body, mind or social messaging to achieve its in-built useful purpose to help adjustments. A 'whirlpool of two loss emotions' is an Emotional Chaos Theory concept new to psychology that has been empirically discovered over many years by using emotional chaos mapping tools with people with a range of psychological and socially disruptive problems. Depending upon which two of the emotional Stepping Stones are interfering with each other's capacity to organise the flow of life constructively, the resulting disorganised whirlpool disturbing the flow of life will have different behavioural and self-belief effects: confusion with fatigue; distress and withdrawal; tension broken by irrational action.

These are normal human existential states, which when pushed to overwhelming extremes can present as common mental illnesses and socially disruptive behaviours: PTSD; chronic fatigue; shame; low self-regard with rumination; OCD with self-harming behaviours or bulimia; destructive drives and suicidal thoughts. All of these can be analysed to derive from the corruption of normal, healthy grieving states when they disrupt each other in an emotional chaos. The solution, however, is simple. By recognising that such a thing as whirlpools in healthy grief emotions can have such effects, a lifelong learning approach to getting constructive feedback into the emotional world can lead to spontaneous self-organisation in a healthier pattern of emotions, that releases personal energy to adjust from where it has been trapped.

Creative conversations that help to de-stress

There is a trick behind the effectiveness of Emotional Logic to transform life and strengthen personal identity. If I were to say to you, “Tell me what your values are”, you would probably look at me as if I had said something odd. But if I say to you, “Tell me, in this situation you face, what you are worried you might lose”, you could probably fairly quickly make a list of 6-12 items.

A ‘Loss Reaction Worksheet’ enables people to list their ‘hidden losses’ in a self-organising way. It is not a morbid process to do this, because a list of hidden losses is, in fact, a list of your previously un-named values. People only know what they value when they see the risk that they might lose it. To go a step further with this idea, the unpleasant emotions of a loss reaction are therefore not negative! Properly understood, they are the evidence that someone has values that are being challenged and need naming… A personal value is psychologically nothing other than that which initiates a loss reaction on detecting the possibility of its loss.

Learning to move in ways that build upon explicit personal values is worth the effort. It is not helpful for humanity to just ‘get rid of’ emotions in order to reason. It is far more important to understand and harness unpleasant emotions for their inbuilt survival and thriving purposes. They point to our hidden values. Conversations that clarify loss emotions and the underlying values that are being challenged will build relationships when they lead on to an agreed action plan that will preserve or recover those named values - that will thus build a future on those explicitly shared human values.

Emotional Logic is a way to make explicit your hidden values, and to build a values-based action plan on just one of them. On-line learning resources available through the Emotional Logic Centre website can start a renewal. They introduce constructive feedback in stressful situations that will bring your emotions and reasoning into a creative partnership, releasing a ‘Butterfly Effect’ of personal development that unpredictably brings renewed well-being and social order from within. Doing so increases simultaneously your capacity to make decisions, your sense of self-efficacy, and your empathic connection with others. That is the outcome of truly emotional self-care.

Loss Action Word Sets

Shock

anxious	panicky
apprehensive	paralysed
cold sweat	overwhelmed
confused	scared
disorientated	shaken
dread	stunned
fearful	trembling
numb	unprepared

Means: I am doubting my resources. I don't know how to cope with this.

Useful purpose: Stop what you are doing! Find a safe place and review your resources.

Denial

ignore it	disclaim
reject	turn away
invalidate	detach
turn a deaf ear	forget it
refuse to believe	carry on
say it's irrelevant	dismiss
evade	disallow
avoid	disown

Means: I can carry on regardless. If I ignore this it will go away.

Useful purpose: Shelve it for now, so I can keep my energy going for what else is important.

Anger

bad-tempered	jealous
bitter	resentful
irritated	spiteful
furious	frustrated
indignant	want revenge
offended	malice
touchy	full of hate
sulky	hold a grudge

Means: I want to prevent the loss of something important to me.

Useful purpose: The energy to take action in the world despite risk and change it.

Guilt

remorse	repentant
blame	want to own up
my fault	soul searching
flawed	self-questioning
full of regret	should do more
mortified	liable
self-reproach	if only
disillusioned	bad conscience

Means: I need to question if something I did caused it.

Useful purpose: Learning! What else could I do that might prevent it happening again?

Bargaining

Aggressive	*Assertive*	*Passive*
break	ask "What if..?"	lie low
barge	ask "If..then..?"	acquiesce
bully	be present	am resigned
corner	convince	apathetic
dominate	declare	be moulded
drive others	endure	concede
feud	influence	get nostalgic
force	inspire	hesitate
grab	motivate	lie low
oppress	negotiate	non-action
poison	offer	play dead
pressure	risk	stagnate
put down	take turns	step back
threaten	team up	submit
vendetta	try	turn shy
	write a letter	wait and see

Means: I must try doing something to get back what has gone that was important.

Useful purpose: The energy to take risks to deal with situations in new ways.

Depression

Suppressed	Subdued
Hopeless	Powerless
Miserable	Ineffective
Useless	Sick at heart
Feel defeated	Flat
Despair	Empty
Care worn	Worthless
Dispirited	Pointless

Means: I seem empty and powerless. This is a place of decision where to go next.

Useful purpose: Seeing my limits might help me to stop trying for the impossible.

Acceptance

Hope	Integrity
Gentleness	Liberation
Joy	Serenity
Self-control	Maturity
Forgiveness	Resolved
Grace	Sadness
Healing	Relief
Moved on	Peace

Means: Joy - I recognise I am powerless over one particular loss, but have discovered in other areas of life I am still creative and valued.

Sadness: I can re-join the human race more maturely, using energy to explore life's opportunities. Life can be ever-renewed.

Jakob Owens, Unsplash

21 Avoiding Desperation and The Men's Seven Questions from Ireland

"**De-speration**" being cast down away from hope (spero: "I hope").

Sometimes we can feel really down and sometimes we feel alone. Doctors are statistically at higher risk of suicide than other professions - but the answers are not difficult. Here are some thoughts:

Suicide happens either in the context of mental illness (depression, psychosis and so on) or in situations of acute emotional overwhelm and distress, especially with a feeling of hopelessness. Many people who self-harm do not want to kill themselves - it can be a 'coping strategy' to deal with overwhelming emotions and psychic pain (NHS Choices[1]). People don't want to be dead for ever, they just want to escape the pain of now.

Antidote: treat mental illness, find support, initiate hope, kindle hope, continue support.

Barriers to seeking help: loss of perspective, hopelessness, shame, loss of face, pride, untreated mental illness. Also for clever minds - loss of insight into own state, often compounded by perfectionism, fear of failure, and the 'imposter syndrome' (which many doctors suffer from at times).

Powerful Medicine: **HOPE. And remember, a state of suicidal crisis WILL pass, and things WILL improve. Do ask for help, and keep asking.**

Prevention aims at: Identification, Intervention, Achieving a safe outcome.

Myths: People who talk about it won't do it. Anyone who tries to kill themselves must be crazy. If they have decided, nothing can stop them. People who complete suicide are unwilling to seek help. Talking about suicide may give someone the idea[2]. **ALL are FALSE**.

A good structure to use is the **ASIST** model:

- **Explore Invitations** - be alert to the clues that a person may be feeling suicidal and may wish to talk (including prolonged pleading eye contact - or avoidance of gaze).
- **Ask about Suicide** - to confirm presence of thoughts and show you are ready to help.
- **Listen** to the reasons for dying and living with respect.
- **Review the Risk**
- **Contract a Safe Plan** which will allow them freedom to think about suicide; will be specific; will have only limited achievable objectives, which are agreed and will arrange crisis support, maintaining a suicide safe environment. This will bring hope and a way forward. Refer, as appropriate, to secondary care.

- Follow up on Commitments - arrange further care, appropriately and speedily.

SAFETool[1] from Connecting with People is a principles-based approach. It enables a compassionate assessment and clear formulation of risk into one of the four categories of passive, active, dangerous, or dangerous and imminent. It then follows on to create a joint safety plan between client and practitioner.

Suicide Prevention Tips:

1. Speak up if you are worried.
2. Respond quickly in a crisis - you could save a life. During your career you will probably help more people than you will ever know.
3. Offer help.[2]

Suicide Help:

1. Find reasons to live.
2. Avoid drugs and alcohol (they disinhibit us).
3. Make the home safe.
4. Take hope - people DO get through this.
5. Share your suicidal feelings with someone else.
6. Make a 'safety plan'.

There are more sources of help available in the appendix.[3]

Health Inequalities for Men and the Seven Key Questions from Ireland

This is not a plea for men being special. Every person deserves care and respect, gender being irrelevant to need. Furthermore, women may suffer just as much, in similar or different ways. However, there still seems to be more of a stigma about mental health amongst men, who find it difficult to talk. This is even more so amongst some ethnic minorities, but is common to many men.

On many parameters, men do worse than women in health. Statistically, their lives are shorter from many illnesses, they have more accidents, indulge in more drug and alcohol taking behaviour, are more likely to enter prison, they experience more physical violence and, notably, they do not talk about it. Men often find it difficult to talk, and commonly fail to seek help. Worse still – we almost expect this in society – there are stereotypes in our thinking that run so deep that we may not challenge them…

Think of a woman in distress. She will (often) attract sympathy. However, a man in distress may not get the same approach, due to the way the distress manifests.

Violence, alcohol abuse, anger and frustration may actually be signs of male distress rather than causative factors themselves. Occasionally the seemingly logical end step of a male in distress is to take his own life. Historically, completed male suicides outweigh those of females, especially by more violent means. Male distress may also manifest in withdrawal and silence, especially if the occupation is solitary (think farming and some aspects of construction).

Men can suffer psychological distress that conflicts with their sense of 'manliness'. Some feel stigmatised. They may not have experienced a rite of passage into adulthood. When it comes to resolving problems, men often engage better in solution focused approaches. Hence the growth of 'Man Sheds' as a movement to build camaraderie and a shared purpose.

Ireland recognised that there was a specific problem during the recent economic crisis, and have therefore invested in solutions and the development of 'a new conversation' about men's health.

The Men's Development Network has created a powerful set of seven key questions which support men to reflect in a coaching style.[4] They are proven to be effective, and could be used widely in UK society as well by professionals:

1. How are things?
2. What's going well?
3. What's not going well?
4. Is there anything you need to do?
5. Is there any support you need?
6. What's one step you might take?
7. What difference might it make?

   Question one should then be returned to again.

(Things, Well, Not, Need to do, Support, Step, Difference) TWNNSSD

This is a proven framework from which to start a conversation. "A trouble shared is a trouble halved" and just stating the issues out loud can be a powerful start towards solving the problems.[5] We owe it to society to support men when they need it. These seven questions apply to all people, not just to men, and can be seen as powerful ways to start a conversation. Certainly, talking about something rather than burying it helps us to find our own answers. Most health professionals can remember a long consultation where the patient spoke a great deal, the professional said little, and at the end the patient said *"Thank you for making everything so clear for me"*.

Reflection points:

- If you felt in desperate circumstances, how or who would you ask for help? What if a colleague hinted at feeling low, how would you follow this up?
- When did you last ask: "how are things going?" or "what's going on?" Did you listen carefully for the answers?
- Has your organisation considered Wellness Action plans?

22 Knowing Yourself: Personality Types and Patterns of Imbalance

'Know Thyself' was inscribed on the Greek Temple at Delphi, along with 'Everything in Moderation'.

We've already looked at some psychological models of how our Software Being works. Other valuable insights come from cultural and historical views and from Jung, Myers-Briggs and Belbin. If we can understand our preferred personality type and preferred role in meetings and groups then we can get the best out of ourselves. This will also help us avoid the feeling of frustration when we are in the wrong role. What is more, we can understand others better - and therefore communicate with them better - to mutual benefit.

Case study
Dr A was a great ideas person and could draft good plans ('reporter/ideas generator' [Belbin]), but had no ability to follow-through. By teaming him with a colleague to discuss the ideas with and look at practical implementation (Sounding Board), a manager who was a good driver of plans ('driver/thruster'), and a secretary and audit clerk who were 'completer-finishers', the department moved forwards effectively.

Personality Types
We all know that people are different from each other. A number of different personality types have been identified:

- Quiet or noisy
- Quick or slow
- Outward going or inward looking
- Strong willed or weak willed
- Peaceful or worriers
- Intuitive or misguided
- Needy or self-assured
- Fearful or courageous
- Aloof or engaging in life
- And others…

The Big Five dimensions of human personality are, according to Daniel Nettle[1] are: extraversion, conscientiousness, neuroticism, agreeableness and openness. We live in the world and act through our personalities, which adds to the variety of life! It gives us lots of experiences to learn from, both about ourselves and about others.

In Medieval times people were thought to be one of, or a mixture of, four types - the **humours**:

- **Sanguine** (blood, related to the element of air) – have lots of energy, and are often cheerful, popular, confident, but can be impulsive and easily distracted.
- **Choleric** (yellow bile, related to fire) – doers and leaders, with lots of energy but easily flare up into anger or become bad tempered.
- **Melancholic** (black bile, related to earth) – can be thoughtful, kind and considerate, creative too but can become drawn into negative emotions of sadness and distress about life's events.
- **Phlegmatic** (phlegm, related to water) – often self-content, relaxed, good observers, but can be shy and so put the dampeners on a group activity.

In Indian Culture, there are three **Doshas**

- **Vata** - the principle of moving, and related to qualities of cold, moving, quick, dry and rough.
- **Pitta** - the principle of transformation, related to qualities of hot, sharp, moist and sour.
- **Kapha** - the principle of holding steady, related to qualities of heavy, sweet, steady and soft.

Every person is either one type dominant, or a mixture of two, or a synthesis of all three, and so expresses different personalities.

Modern psychologists have explained human behaviour in personality types:

Jung considered that people were either mainly Extraverted or Introverted (though we are all a mix of both)

- Extroverts direct their attention and energy outward into the world and towards objects and other people.
- Introverts tend to focus their attention more within and explore the subjective experience of the world, rather than having outward attachments.

Jung went on to define four functions of a person: 'thinking', 'feeling', 'sensation', and 'intuition'. Each person can have one of these as a predominant way of experiencing the world, thus becoming their personality type.

Philip Bailey[2] notes that Jung's types correspond to medieval humours:

Element	Jungian type	Positive aspects	Negative aspects	Lack of element
Earth	Sensation-oriented	Realistic, practical, reliable, intuitive connection to earth	Materialistic, narrow-minded, inflexible	Unrealistic, impractical, impulsive
Air	Intellectual	Intellectual, objective, detached, broadminded	Over-analytical, insensitive, aloof	Fuzzy thinking, subjective, attachment
Fire	Inspired, Intuitive	Confidence, independence, inspiration, assertive	Arrogant, selfish, delusions of grandeur, angry	Timidity, lack of self-worth, apathy, passive
Water	Emotional	Sensitive, intuitive, nurturing	Oversensitive, subjective, dependent	Insensitive, superficial, cold

Myers Briggs[3] developed this further into the famous Myers Briggs Type inventory, which honours the fact that we are different. The tool assesses people and places them into one of sixteen types, depending on whether they use:

- Extraversion or Introversion
- Sensing or Intuition
- Thinking or Feeling
- Judging or Perceiving

For instance ENFP are good with 'ideas' and 'people' – ('People' is about seeing everything as related, wanting to be liked and to help others [little pleasers]). They genuinely like people and show it!

By contrast, certain of the 'I' types have no need to chat or waste time in idle pursuits and feel secure internally and comfortable with silence. Some others may interpret this behaviour as disinterested, rude or uncommunicative but it is actually the way the other person just is and that is OK!

On the web, there are a number of free tools that can help us assess our personality type – worth doing every so often in our careers to remind us of how and who we are and also how our skillset may suit specific roles.[4]

Honey and Mumford[5] distinguish four types of people:

- **Activists** like action, the here and now and immediate challenges. They may be talkative. They are open-minded but get easily bored with implementing plans or changes that are not immediate. They can jump quickly to conclusions which are not always correct.
- **Reflectors** take a detached view, gather information, consider carefully and analyse, wait before reaching a conclusion, are thoughtful and make good listeners.
- **Theorists** use logic to consider an issue step by step, are objective, like to make theories from a collection of facts or observations and tend to be serious. They may find subjective approaches and light heartedness irritating.
- **Pragmatists** like to find and test new ideas and approaches, are practical and grounded and enjoy quick problem solving and decision making. They may be bored with long discussions.

Which type are you? There are questionnaires on the web[6] which can help.

Healing

Other ways of looking at personalities come from a healing perspective - that is to say - what are the "tuning forks" that can help this particular person be better, strengthen their qualities, and shine out as a person?

Dr Edward Bach, originator of Bach Flower Remedies[7], suggested that there are twelve great personality types, depending upon the soul lesson we have come to earth to learn. For each, there is a flower which can help support us in our growth through this lesson. Thus, Agrimony helps retune restless people who put a brave face on things, and are learning the inner lesson of 'peace', Impatiens supports quick-minded, easily irritated people who are developing the quality of 'patience', Centaury brings about the development of the quality of saying 'no' in people who are a pushover and will always agree to do something for others, even if it's not in their own best interests.

Dr Bach felt that for each person, one of these essences which would resonate with their inner being and bring health. The Twelve Healers and Dr Bach's Soul Lessons are:

- Agrimony - Peace (overcomes restlessness)
- Centaury - Strength (overcomes Weakness)
- Cerato - Wisdom (overcomes Ignorance)
- Chicory - Love (overcomes Possessiveness)
- Clematis - Gentleness (overcomes Indifference)
- Gentian - Understanding (overcomes Doubt)

- Impatiens - Forgiveness (overcomes Impatience)
- Mimulus - Sympathy (overcomes Fear)
- Rock Rose - Courage (overcomes Terror)
- Scleranthus - Steadfastness to Life's purpose (overcomes Indecision)
- Vervain - Tolerance (overcomes Over-Enthusiasm)
- Water Violet - Joy (overcomes Grief)

If this sounds a bit airy-fairy, and not for you, no matter, these are all models that work for some people, especially those who are sensitive to atmospheres and emotions. There are some proprietary Bach Remedy combinations that make it easy to try them out - some people find Calm Down good for work stress, Cheer Up good for the glooms, and a busy Ward Sister found that Get Up and Go helped her stay refreshed on nights, needing less Red Bull than before! They only work for some people, not all. To help us choose, several makers produce a variety of combinations.

Scleranthus © Julian Barnard

Cerato © Julian Barnard

Gentian © Julian Barnard

Water Violet Julian Barnard

23 Preventative Medicine and the Inner Smile

Dr William Bloom

Visiting my GP a little while ago he began talking with me about his own health. This was not unusual as we had known each other for twenty years and he had read my self-help book The Endorphin Effect[1]. He was committed to a holistic approach and believed that good medicine enabled patients into self-care.

"If only I had practised what I preach," he said wryly, "I would have caught my own condition much earlier and probably avoided surgery. "

We then chatted for a while about the archetype of the wounded healer and the self-sacrificing hero and that medics have a calling to relieve the suffering of others, but not themselves. Self-care is hardly on the clinical map and hardly possible in a busy day.

"You could do the self-examination in the bath or lying in bed or even commuting to work," I nudged. "You know exactly where to scan."

He sighed. He agreed. He then had to see more patients and I left.

The interesting thing for me about clinicians is that, of all people, you know how to scan a body for signs of ill health. You know the crucial importance of early diagnosis and appropriate adjustments in behaviour, diet, exercise and life style. *But you rarely do it for yourself*. When you examine patients you get a quick sense of their state from their body posture, skin tone, breathing and the state of their eyes. *But you rarely do it for yourself.* With careful hands and appropriate kit you touch, push, look, listen and feel. You know all the signs of ill health. *But...*

More than that, before any physical examination you ask the core question, 'How do you feel?' *But...*

Again - and I know that I am repeating myself but it bears this repetition - because it is your profession you know exactly what to scan for and what signs are important, but in failing to self-examine you continually risk your own physical and mental health.

So, how do you feel?

Your main piece of kit here is your own mental ability to scan, sense and cognise what it feels like inside your body. This requires the self-discipline of an intentional pause and then deliberately focusing down into your own physicality.

This sensory, 'felt' awareness of yourself is crucial. It is the sovereign individual who alone can really know and experience their own state; and is able to self-assess and catch early signs of threatening symptoms. Who else can notice those signals that require just a tad of relevant adjustment: a bit more exercise, regular stretching, earlier nights, less caffeine, better food, more fresh air?

Being very serious and also pragmatic, surely the long-term viability of the NHS is based in this self-awareness, early diagnosis and preventative self-care?

Self-care as preventative medicine is not of course a new model. Indeed in classical Chinese medicine the art of being in a friendly clinical relationship with your own body is considered the foundation of good health. There is even a clear set of instructions on precisely how to conduct this practice. At its heart is a relaxed and friendly bedside manner towards your own physicality.

Sometimes this self-care practice is translated from Chinese as the 'inner smile', which may sound quirky to a cynical ear, a prime candidate for a bad science award. But unpack the 'inner smile' tolerantly and we can see that it meshes extremely well with a modern understanding of the integration of brain, nervous system, endocrine system and gut ecology.

The 'inner smile' is in fact a good example of psychoneuroimmunology (PNI) and polyvagal theory put into practice. The practitioner is advised to do it daily and when the body is at ease, with a particular focus on letting the abdomen drop down and sink into relaxation. With a calm and friendly attitude the practitioner then conducts an internal scan, especially checking in on all the major organs and noticing how they feel. Moreover the practitioner is asked to come into a direct and personal relationship with each organ, greeting it with a smile.

Is this hippy-dippy? Anyone with the slightest knowledge of mind-body anatomy and PNI will understand that this internal focus triggers signals from the brain through the nervous system into the endocrine system. It is crucial therefore that the practitioner's attitude be friendly. If the self-examination is conducted with a purely clinical, impatient or, worst, an inquisitorial attitude, the message triggered in the neuro-endocrinal system will be that of threat, thereby precipitating the production of cortisol and adrenalin. If however the attitude is friendly and comfortingly parental then the neural signal is reassuring and soothing, triggering a cocktail of wellbeing hormones: endorphins, oxytocin and serotonin. Just as an external caring parent can do wonders for our health, so an internal caring persona can have a similar positive effect.

Scanning with the Inner Smile then serves two purposes:

- It brings into conscious awareness the felt state of your own body; early diagnosis leading to appropriate early intervention.
- It self-soothes, relaxing and opening up tissue, integrating heart rate variability, settling and balancing gut ecology - all of which support general good health and a strong immune system.

Done on a daily basis the benefits are obvious.

But people are predictably human and, despite how sensible and positive this practice is, there is resistance to adopting it. I opened this piece with that conversation with my GP who was bemoaning that he had not followed his own advice and caught an early diagnosis of his own illness. He provides an excellent example of the many clinicians and carers who fail to self-care even though they know precisely how to do it and how beneficial it is for them.

So why is there this resistance? Why do professionals who preach self-care and the importance of early intervention completely ignore their own advice? In my opinion it is good to be realistic about the sources of this self-sabotage, because recognising them makes them easier to manage. So here are a few possibilities. See which ones might apply to you.

Why I don't self-care:

- Can't break old habits.
- New behaviour to learn.
- It wasn't in my training.
- Embarrassing and awkward to care for self.
- Internalised authority figure judging you for appearing soft and narcissistic.
- Pretend there is not enough time.
- Frightened to look at what might be wrong.
- Addicted to role of stoic hero and healer.
- Scared of feeling feelings.
- Lazy and lack discipline.
- Depressed and no motivation.

Those are all extremely good and normal reasons for avoiding self-care.

What therefore might motivate someone to push through the resistance? We could just wait for a harsh health crisis to prod you into action - the 'stick'. Or - and I write this carefully after decades of experience in the field - you could just exercise *sensible self-discipline*, similar to washing your hands after the loo. I have led hundreds of trainings and I really know that other than the unpleasant shock of a severe illness, the only thing that seems to work is a disciplined rhythm that ultimately, like hand-washing, becomes a part of your normal life style. The 'carrots' of self-care and early intervention are obvious.

To summarise:
Be encouraged as a professional by the skills and knowledge you already bring to self-care.

Your Skills and Knowledge:

- Physiology.
- Body awareness.
- Necessity of early intervention.
- Good bedside manner.
- High awareness of the basic strategies for general good health.
- High awareness of the immediate ameliorating strategies for specific health challenges.
- Importance of modelling self-care for others.
- Congruence.
- Scientific understanding of the neuro-endocrinal mechanism and benefits of the Inner Smile self-care practice.

And do the practice.

Inner Smile Self-Care
Daily - perhaps in bed; lunch break; watching television; whenever suits you:

- Allow your body to sink down into being at ease.
- Let your abdomen slump and let your breath soften.
- Switch on the attitude of good bedside manner, like a friendly parent.
- Focus down into your own body and scan it.
- In whatever sequence works for you, give awareness to and feel into each organ and each region; sense into your systems.
- Notice how it all feels and the indications.
- Think about the appropriate health benefiting activities.
- Action the appropriate health benefiting activities.

The long-term benefits for you and your community are immense.

Reflection points:
- What is the Inner Smile?
- How does it feel?
- How long does it take you to do this each day?
- Will you share this with others?

Dr Jeremy Swayne is a retired GP, Church of England priest, and author of Remodelling Medicine[1] , which explores a holistic approach and vision for health and health care.

Spirituality and the uniqueness of life

At the heart of my work as a doctor, and more recently as a priest, has been a desire that perhaps we all share: to affirm the unique significance, value and meaning of every person's life and to help to mitigate, to some extent, whatever limits the fulfilment of that promise.

For me, this is underpinned by the knowledge that each one of us is uniquely loved and valued by the creative and sustaining power that many of us call God; by the desire to enhance people's experience of that love and by the conviction that every one of us has a unique and indispensable part to play in completing the bigger picture and unfolding narrative of life that Christians call 'the Kingdom of God'.

This sense of the significance, value and meaning of a unique life within that bigger picture is central to what we mean by 'wholeness' and is the essence of the spirituality that is indispensable to that wholeness. This is not so different, I am sure, from many other people's understanding of spirituality and wholeness. The Royal College of Psychiatrists' spirituality special interest group, for example, says much the same thing: *"Spirituality - an experience of meaning, purpose, belonging, integration and wholeness; linking the deeply personal with the universal; not necessarily associated with formal religion, culture or belief in God."*[2]

Like personality and sexuality, (and intimately involved with them) spirituality is an aspect of our common humanity; a thread that runs through the tapestry of our lives, not an optional extra or an acquired attribute. It is an intrinsic and essential reality of our human nature.

I expect this much is common ground for most of us when we think about personal wholeness, but I found it to be a practical challenge for me in the early years of my GP career.

Human Wholeness

I created this diagram after about 10 years in general practice to help me respond as best I could to the mixed dynamics of my patients' problems. It represents my understanding of what it is to be human; of all that goes to make us what we are. The three familiar dimensions of human nature - body, mind and soul - have the core attributes shown in the respective circles. Each is subject to the influences shown around the perimeter. The overlapping areas show the processes by which each aspect of our being interacts with another, emphasising the intimacy with which each relates to the whole. It is intended to be truly holistic in representing this totality. The soul and the spiritual life are integral to this pattern. Its essential character is the complete integration of every aspect of human nature that it represents. There are no separate compartments. Whatever the focus of illness, pain or disability, whatever the circumstances from which it arises, it affects the person as a whole and must be treated as a whole.

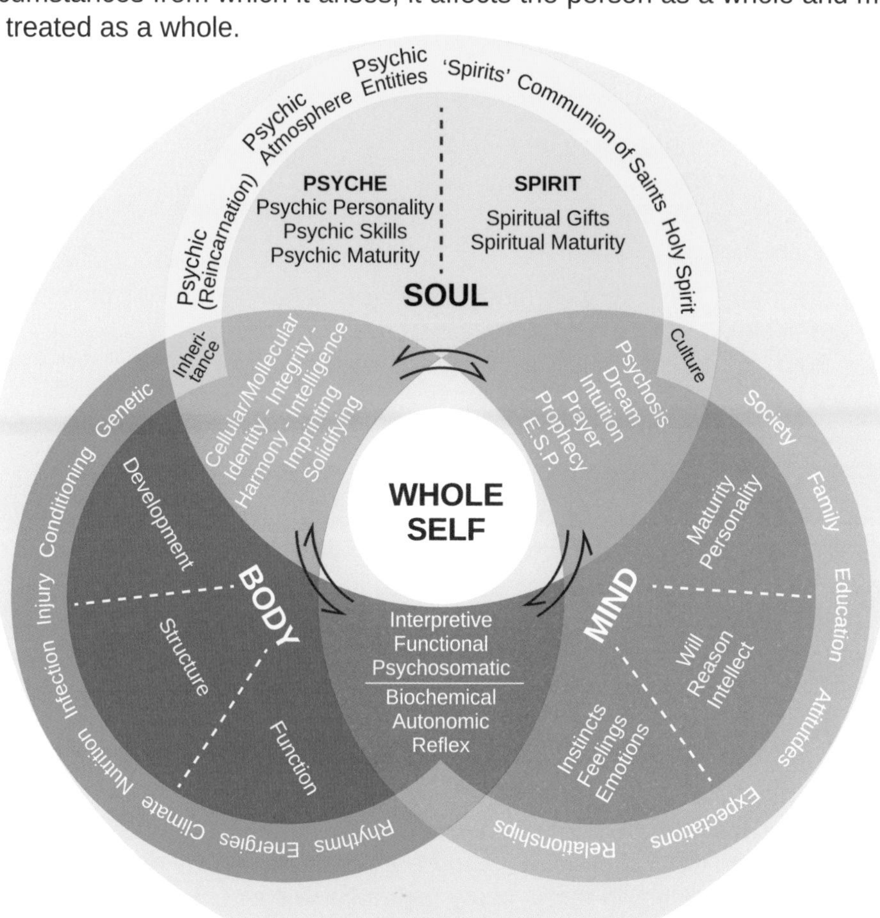

24.1

The Soul

In creating this picture, two things led me to seek a better understanding of the nature of the soul as a clinical reality, so to speak. One was an emerging sensitivity to certain psychic phenomena and an awareness of the psychic dimension of human nature. The other was the realisation that there are wounds to the psyche that are not accessible to psychological help alone. This is a judgement based not just on my own psychological insights, but on the fact that over the years I have seen patients who have clearly benefited from the mature psychological skills of others, but without their wounds being healed or their suffering relieved. I interpret these as wounds to the soul, and have found that a greater degree of healing is achieved when this is recognised, acknowledged and responded to appropriately. I know that I am not alone in this view.[3]

The soul has been described as "the information bearing essence" that expresses the unique identity of the person.[4] I have come to understand it as the interpenetrating relationship of psyche and spirit, formed by and informing every experience of our lives; our psychic nature and attributes infused by the Spirit, the divine nature, God, the Life Force - whatever term is congenial to you.

In the diagram I have represented this essence as comprising psyche and spirit but deciding what we mean by psyche is a problem. Part of the difficulty arises from the various uses of the words psyche and psychic. The Greek word psyche has entered the English language and acquired a life of its own. Not only does it have to accommodate the concepts of *psyche* in modern psychology, but also the phenomena that are commonly described as psychic.

The psychic dimension of our nature has been called the "intermediate dimension"[5] - intermediate between mind and spirit. It embraces the unconscious elements of our personality, and the collective unconscious described by Carl Jung. It includes those attributes that are described as extrasensory or paranormal. There is a tendency to melodramatise the psychic dimension, but it is worth remembering that electricity was regarded as occult before its true nature was understood.

Our Spiritual Life

I experience the loving and creative power that sustains life as a personal relationship with God and believe it to be a relationship that is common to all of us; to all humankind. In terms of my faith, I know it as Christ and to have an active principle called 'the Holy Spirit' that energises, guides and inspires me. From this derives my 'enthusiasm' for life; my enthousiamos - whose Greek root means 'possessed by a God'.

Although I am confident in the Christian affirmation that 'God is; and he is as he is in Jesus', I do not hold with the exclusively masculine identity of God, nor with an exclusive Christian attitude to the nature of Christ. I agree with a wise

Nun of my acquaintance that "...we can't believe that the whole of humankind has to join the Christian Church. God is much larger than that".[6] And with the theologian Austin Farrer that, "That is not to say that the Holy Spirit has no scope of action in any but Christian hearts. There is, as it were, a Christ-factor where there is not Christ".[7]

Fundamentally, however, we construe it according to our particular insights or traditions - spirituality is an innate and integral aspect of our human nature and essential to our unique identity as a person.

This is one reason why spirituality is central to healing - for ourselves as well as for others. We cannot be fully well, whole, integrated (if any of us ever are) while there is dissonance between the life we live and what I would call our unique vocation; that is, becoming the person we uniquely have it in us to be. True knowledge of that vocation, however seemingly ordinary or exalted it may be, resides only in the soul.

Its fulfilment may be thwarted by many things: our circumstances; the expectation, teaching or attitudes of others; our own misplaced desires or ambition and so on. Like a jigsaw puzzle that will fail or buckle if pieces are misplaced, our lives will suffer if the pieces that should make us who we truly are, are missing, misplaced, damaged, or displaced by other pieces that do not belong to the picture.

It is through our spiritual life that we can feel our way towards the knowledge and fulfilment of our vocation, and the wholeness that comes with it. Religion should nourish that spiritual experience and insight. Too often, as Jesus of course repeatedly pointed out, it does the reverse; committing the sin that I call 'doctrine abuse'; as destructive to health and wellbeing as any other abuse; perhaps more so.

And spirituality is central to healing because it is our spiritual life; that relationship with the divine that will help to heal our own wounds and through us the wounds of others. Whether it be through prayer, loving kindness, good intention, or whatever therapeutic gifts and skills we may be endowed with.

"God grant me the serenity to accept the things I cannot change, the courage to change the things I can, and the wisdom to know the difference."

Reinhold Niebuhr

Dr Maya Roberts, Mindfulness Teacher and former Consultant Psychiatrist, co-author of the Royal College of Psychiatrists' 2018 Position Statement on Sustaining Doctors' Mental Health.

In the hectic rush of a busy life, we don't often stop to contemplate and act upon what we need to do to be in the best shape possible to meet the constant stream of everyday ups and downs, demands and challenges. In particular, we don't ask what can help our brain to be in the best shape possible, even if we give our body a healthy diet and take regular exercise. Here are three tips for optimal brain functioning:

1. **Adequate hydration** is essential. Being dehydrated by just 2% impairs performance in tasks that require attention, psychomotor, and immediate memory skills.[1] Dehydration diminishes alertness and concentration. It is a potent cause of irritability or feeling tense; on edge. It can cause headaches or trigger a migraine. Feeling drowsy or irritable? - drink a glass of water.

2. **Physical activity** is the best way to manage stress, according to a large body of research evidence. Since the activities and populations studied are varied, no particular type or time period stands out. Anything from walking to dancing; jogging to swimming or yoga can all be beneficial. It does not have to involve going to a gym - do whatever you find enough motivation to enjoy and to stick with on a regular basis.

3. **Learning to meditate** can counteract the effects of stress at both psychological and neurological levels. Practising mindfulness meditation is, in essence, a brain training programme. This understanding is derived from studies showing neuroplastic changes in brain anatomy (e.g. increased cell density) and CNS activity after a period of regular mindfulness practice.[2]

What is mindfulness?

UK expert Mark Williams, Emeritus Professor of Clinical Psychology at Oxford University, says that mindfulness is:

"The awareness that emerges through paying attention on purpose, in the present moment, with compassion and open-hearted curiosity."[3]

An intellectual understanding of what mindfulness is, gleaned from reading about it or hearing talks, does not take one very far. It is a state of awareness that has to be experienced first-hand; something to know rather than to know about. With accurate instruction, for example, from a class teacher in person or via the internet or CDs, it is easy to experience mindfulness. There is a useful CD of guided practices (short and long) in Mark Williams's widely acclaimed book.[4]

Mindfulness is an inherent human trait. It is even enshrined in the traffic law of "driving with due care and attention"! In developing our capacity to be mindful, we are not attempting any special mental gymnastics into unfathomable new territory, nor straying into religion. What is needed is for our attention to be redirected frequently in daily life in a focused and intentional way rather than being left to roam indiscriminately through past and future, pulled hither and thither by every successive thought, event, TV image, or emotional reaction. Wandering attention is the default mode for the brain when not engaged in a specific task.[2] Mindfulness involves taking conscious control of our own attention, in a gentle, non-striving way that gives the brain a rest from ceaseless activity, as evidenced by EEG studies of meditators.[5]

Presence is perhaps a more useful word than mindfulness. We can learn to pay full attention to what is happening in the moment rather than living life at arm's length through inhabiting a two-dimensional world of concepts. They have their place, obviously, in intellectual pursuits but they tend to crowd in on everything we do. Do I need to repeat to myself *"What a beautiful flower!"* or can I actually let that flower's beauty touch me, absorb the feelings it engenders, really look at it and drink in its beauty? Words become unnecessary when we can stop long enough for a direct experience to blossom. Being outdoors in nature or with our children and pets are prime times to let in, feel and be nourished by the magic of life through being absorbed in the experiences that life brings.

Neuroscience has shown that if we do spend 20-30 seconds connecting with some enjoyable experience - maybe listening to a blackbird singing its song - then the brain treats that positive experience as important and transfers the memory into longterm storage, over time building up a bank of positive memories which create a brighter 'internal climate'.[6] This bank can be available as a resource to draw on to counterbalance our blinkered vision when stressed. None of this can happen if we don't notice the blackbird, beautiful view or other enjoyable event in the first place. Mindfulness is all about noticing. What you do with what you notice is your own business.

When our thoughts are a constant cascade of shoulds, musts and oughts - exhausting lists of things to be remembered and got through - life often feels unfulfilling. By applying ourselves mindfully to very ordinary tasks like doing the washing up, walking, taking a shower, putting on our shoes and so on, it is possible to discover a depth and richness to what used to be hurried through or was barely noticed in the rush to get on to the next moment and to something more important in life.

When we stop to notice what is going on with ourselves, a world of choice opens up. Noticing can be directed to something we want to change:

There I am slumped in front of the computer again - straighten up... I'm getting uptight - *I had better calm down, getting angry will only make this situation worse... I hadn't realised how thirsty I've become - time for a cuppa...*

There are so many ways to make mindfulness work for your benefit; what we neglect in our busy days, caring for others, is to stop for a few seconds and take notice of how we ourselves are doing. People in healthcare professions often feel that to do so is selfish. But if we don't look after ourselves we shall become increasingly less effective at looking after others. In burnout, for example, people lose the capacity to feel caring and compassionate; work diminishes to a hollow act that is unrewarding and far less effective. By practising mindfulness, we are more able to pay close attention to thoughts, feelings and body sensations as they arise and therefore to be more connected to how life impacts us at any given moment. This enables us to manage life better through wise choices that promote health and wellbeing, if we so desire.

What are the benefits of learning mindfulness?

Numerous research studies support positive results such as greater clarity of thinking, greater attention and focus on tasks, leading to better performance at work. Emotional development can take place, with people becoming less reactive and more able to remain on an even keel. Anxiety is diminished and mood improves. These are the results in healthy populations[7] but mindfulness has also helped people cope with their illness in a large number of illness conditions, with especial benefit in the areas of chronic pain, anxiety and depression.[8]

Research into mindfulness for medical students and doctors shows potential benefits relating to stress and burnout and enhanced empathy in relationships with patients.[9]

How does mindfulness combat stress reactions?

Mindful breathing practice switches off sympathetic drive and reinstates parasympathetic dominance, within a few minutes. Relaxation is a side-effect of mindfulness practices. Regular mindfulness meditation affects activity in the limbic system, downregulating the amygdala and attenuating emotional arousal.[10] The neuroplastic effects of mindfulness meditation take time to develop, and argue against the sporadic use of mindfulness such as cherry-picking one or two mindfulness techniques without the support of a regular practice.

What is the best way to learn mindfulness?

Research studies investigating the benefits of mindfulness have used the 8 week Mindfulness-Based Stress Reduction (MBSR) programme as the gold standard for learning mindfulness. The programme teaches meditation and short mindfulness practices to carry out in daily life. The benefits achieved require a daily meditation practice of around 30 minutes. As all of that can be too much of an ask, people have turned to less formal ways to learn mindfulness and to shorter practice times, with a small but promising evidence base[11] compared with hundreds of studies supporting classroom based MBSR programmes in a wide variety of settings.[12] In particular, the app Headspace (www.headspace.com) is very popular worldwide and is now backed by the BMA. For those who want a more substantial training, an internet search should show you where MBSR classes are available in your town or area, or go to https://bemindful.co.uk/learn-mindfulness/ for a postcode-based list of teachers.

If you are suffering with recurrent depression, consider Mindfulness-Based Cognitive Therapy (MBCT). This builds upon the MBSR programme to include some cognitive therapy exercises as well. Research studies[13] have shown that MBCT is as effective as maintenance antidepressants in preventing depressive relapses, as is recognised in the NICE guidelines for the treatment of depression.[14] NHS provision may be patchy but there are also private therapists.

With both teachers and therapists, it is essential to vet their credentials and training - properly trained MBSR or MBCT teachers/therapists will have attended a teacher training programme from an organisation accredited by the UK Network of Mindfulness Teacher Training Organisations.

Reflection points:

- How could mindfulness help you?

Mind, movement and meditation are all linked. Regular practices such as Mindfulness, Yoga and Tai Chi are enjoyable and can result in a state of calm, deep relaxation and peace of mind. This restores our energy and a general state of well-being. Yoga philosophy is the intelligent conscious effort by a person to help achieve inner peace and help discover inner truth.

- Which practices might you try?
- How might you make these into a habit?

26 Changing Weather Fast: The Breath, CtrlAltDelete and Grumpy Fingers

Our 'weather' is our current emotional state. It can be sunny, gloomy, rainy, upset, calm, and so on. We often project our negative weather at others or spend a lot of energy holding it tight inside.

How much better to change it quickly? Note: these techniques may only work for surface weather, not deep. They address a variety of hardware body and software being issues; remember that hardware and software are intertwined, so changing one changes the other.

The Breath

Our breath is what connects us to the outside world of air and oxygen. Observing it can tell us about ourselves. Is it shallow, erratic, rapid and upper chest? (sympathetic drive of anxiety). Is it slow, rhythmic and from the diaphragm? (Parasympathetic oasis of calm).

Choosing to change our breath pattern, then, will entrain the relevant emotional state - really strange, but true!

Let's just make a deposit into the 'bank of health' and 'inner peace'. Feel free to sit on an upright chair with both feet on floor, in a relaxed posture, back feeling comfortable, and allow yourself to take three slow regular rhythmic breaths (through your nose) from the diaphragm (abdominal breathing). Notice how you feel! How often would you like to make a deposit like this? Some practitioners do it between each consultation!

Re-entraining our breathing to harmony and calm can change weather effectively. And then we are 'present'!

Being Present

How often are we actually 'present'? I don't mean just in the physical sense, but with our minds as well. And how often are we just 'sort of there', half-listening, paying only a quarter of our attention, whilst our minds are really elsewhere?

To be truly 'present', we have to be present in the here and now, aware with all our senses, present with our mind; allowing ourselves to be a channel for spirit, a vehicle for our souls. For how often are we 'absent' – only half here, day dreaming elsewhere?

Dissociation, or 'splitting off' is sometimes a protective mechanism to spare us the pain or the hardship of the here and now. However, the experience, sooner or later, will still have to be processed. So, day dreaming may be fine at times, but not as a habit for most of the time or as a way of avoiding issues forever.

When we are present, we are here, now, witnessing life, participating fully, and engaged in the flow of life. When we are not present, or only partially present, we lose the benefits of being present and find ourselves stuck in worries from the past, or projected into anxieties about the future. These are only thoughts but they can seriously affect us and our health! Returning to the 'breath' is a very powerful way of becoming present and centered.

The whole tradition of Yoga and other practices can help us in these issues.

CtrlAltDelete and Grumpy Fingers

Normally, feelings flow effortlessly from state to state and resolve back to detached normality. Sometimes, we get stuck in a particular 'state' and that's when we need help. Luckily, help is at hand - literally!

Many people have heard of acupuncture - the long-established art of placing needles on particular points on the body to influence health positively, by bringing about balance. It's thought that acupuncture points are far from random, as different electrical potentials are present on the skin at these points. It's thought that different points are connected in lines of 'meridians' and that each has a particular influence on the body.

Now each of us has a 'body', and a 'being': hardware, and software. It's thought that the two are intimately interconnected and that using acupuncture works to rebalance software discord – to release blocked information flow. When our software is in harmony, then our hardware works better and we feel healthier.

Acupressure is the use of finger pressure on acupuncture points to achieve a similar effect - though this may be less profound than needles. However, most of us don't carry needles with us and even if we did, using them in public is a bit noticeable really!

CC Breathe Brandworks

Helpfully, on either side of the base of every finger and thumb are acupressure points that work to rebalance the body's software balance - it may have benefits on hardware as well, but it's the software effects we're concerned with here.

So, whenever we find ourselves out of balance, or stuck in a particular frame of mind, finding the right acupressure points can release the stuck state and allow us to get back towards balance. I say towards, because sometimes we carry several layers of imbalance and releasing one stuck state reveals the layer beneath. It's only when you've dealt with all the layers that you're back in balance.

How does it work? Goodness only knows, but sometimes it does!

So how do we do it? Simply pinch one of your finger nails at the base (nearer the palm) of the nail, on either side (not front to back) between the thumb and index finger of the other hand and something happens. Well, it does if you're squeezing the correct nail! Lightly, not tightly.

Exercise

Now, let's practice. Pretend you are upset (not, angry, but distressed, and just upset, not with anything in mind), and try squeezing you left thumbnail. Anything happen? No? - well, no surprise - it doesn't work for most other people either. Now try the index finger, now the middle, now the ring, and finally the little. Spend about 5-10 seconds each time. So which one works for you? Back to the upset state. For me, middle finger left hand shifts that feeling and often, below that state is feeling sorry for myself (left little), and sadness (left ring). If I feel angry, such as when cut up in traffic, then middle and ring fingers of right hand seem to shift the state (and very often below the judgment of anger, is a personal feeling of inadequacy (left little and ring).

The other day, I saw a woman of 25 who had felt 'down' for years. She was the fourth in a large family, and had always felt one down in life, mixed with quite a bit of anger. After gaining her trust (she'd spent several years in institutions), she let me show her how Grumpy Fingers might help. Within minutes, she could feel things improving as her perspective changed. From a frightened child, rocking herself in front of me, she quickly started to take control and responsibility for herself. She gave a smile as she knew that here was something for her – something she could really use in life to smooth out the bumps and help her grow. Sometimes it's the obstacles in life's way that prevent us from gaining the benefit from our experiences and moving forward. I trust that this young lady will now do well.

The fun comes when you start practicing with all sorts of states and then you find you can resolve them quickly, without anyone else noticing. All sorts of people have found how helpful it is to them, and considering that it is often stuck feelings that cause wayward or out of balance behaviour, it's worth resolving the little things as soon as you notice them. Often the 'dog' of our behaviour is being wagged by the 'tail' of an unresolved feeling, but why should we let it?

Sometimes we can spend years holding on to old patterns of thoughts and feelings and for some of them, the answer is in our own hands - literally! Why not try it out - and have some fun?

A sophisticated **Ctrl+Alt+Delete** it to intertwine all our fingers, so that nail base touches nail base (may require some practice). CtrlAltDelete and three slow deep breaths from your tummy. This will centre and rebalance you into the calm of the 'here' and 'now' of your inner being.

CC Breathe Brandworks

CC Breathe Brandworks

Acupressure point Pericardium 6 (Nei Guan) is another useful one. On the ventral surface of the wrist, between the two long flexor tendons it is three fingers' breadth back from the carpal bones towards the elbow. It is useful for nausea (including chemotherapy), motion sickness and some headaches.

Reflection points:

- How might acupressure work? (hint, think software retuning)
- Consider learning more about this - how would you start?
- What other tools could you use for inner balance?
- Consider exploring a judgment / thought that you hold with steady acupressure on each of your fingers /thumbs, and notice when it changes.
- How does it change?
- Are there any other layers of judgment (about others or about yourself) that are underpinning this thought?

Personal Growth

Nature can help heal humanity, if humanity wishes. “O do not step upon the flower, but listen what she says.” [1]

“The kiss of the sun for pardon, the song of the birds for mirth, you’re nearer God’s heart in a garden, than anywhere else on earth.” [2]

Mankind is deeply connected to nature at a psychological level, especially when present and mindful. “By connecting with Nature, we discover our own inner nature”. Human Beings are amazingly created/creative creations/ devices to allow consciousness to explore the experiences of being in matter / the material world. Modern physics tells us that everything is connected and that everything is made from patterns of vibration. Fractal geometry shows us that life evolves in harmonious patterns. Sometimes patterns of information develop an imbalance and then become distorted, showing this distortion in our thoughts and feelings.

In ideal development, the soul goes through experiences and develops qualities of character, such as courage, restraint, inner peace, love, steadfastness to purpose, confidence, good cheer, optimism and so on. Sometimes, through reaction to adversity or going off track, the soul develops the opposite to a quality - an imbalance. These include impatience, hatred, lack of confidence, fear, loneliness or others.

From childhood our spontaneity steadily shuts down to conform. How many ‘no’s’, ‘shouldn’ts’, ‘can’ts’ do we hear as children? Add to this the possibility of abuse, be it physical, emotional or sexual. Then many of us have suffered bereavements, divorces, relationship break-ups, the effects of affairs, alcoholism or drug abuse. Nevertheless, if you ask most adults in the street how they are - what do they say? “fine”. Fine! (Fearful, Insecure, Neurotic and Emotionally Imbalanced). This conventional answer underlines the fact that most of us don’t even want to acknowledge the buried pain of the past we all carry because we all accept it as normal!

Flower Essences Use

Many people use Five Flower or Rescue Remedy for shock or distress. However, there are 38 Bach Flower Essences and many others from around the world. Flower Essences are harmonious patterns of information from nature that can retune these imbalances, and enhance and expand aspects of our consciousness. They enable us to achieve greater insights, wisdom and maturity in our personal development. They work upon our ‘software being’, not on our ‘hardware body’, in a way similar to music retuning aspects of our selves, to help us feel better and perform better. Used proactively, they have been called the "effortless tools of personal development". Well, nothing's quite that easy, but they certainly can help a great deal!

Dr Edward Bach discovered his Flower Remedies in the 1930s. He chose twelve soul types (The Twelve Healers), seven for patterns of chronic illness (the Seven Helpers) and the final nineteen, for reactive states of emotion to particular circumstances. He discovered that taking them developed our 'virtues' and he hoped that by doing so, disease would be driven out by the increase in health. Nowadays we recognise that essences are valuable tools for the software being, but we would not expect any direct effect upon the physical body.

Bach Flower Essences are made by several makers, including Healing Herbs, Sun Essences, Crystal Herbs and Ainsworths. They are widely available and use brandy as a carrier. In the brandy is information transcribed from nature - incredible, perhaps - but no more than a round silver disc (a CD) having music or photographs on it - encoded, of course, as information! This information, like music, acts to retune our feelings and other bits of our invisible software that are out of balance. Put drops into each drink, or onto your tongue, or make up a treatment bottle and watch yourself change!

What are Flower Essences for?

Flower Essences are powerful vibrational catalysts to transform negative emotions into positive. By taking essences appropriate to the emotional aspect that is out of balance, transformation can occur. 'Emotional broken glass' that has been unresolved for years, let alone months can sometimes be relatively swiftly transformed. For instance, Holly can transform jealousy, envy, suspicion and greed into a loving aspect, as I found out over just three days in a two-year-old child suffering from toddler jealousy. Children often respond rapidly; adults rather more slowly. In another case, a six-year-old's night terrors resolved after less than a week of taking Rock Rose.

Any one can use them and they are compatible with all prescribed medication. They are not a substitution for good sleep (free from electromagnetic fields), exercise, optimal nutrition and so on, but work alongside to help us feel better in life, and transit life's learning lessons with ease. Dr Bach advised them not to be used in cases of psychosis (there are other things going on). I would add: they are not an alternative treatment for mental illness to orthodox approaches. However, in minor emotional disorders, they may have a supportive place to play under medical supervision. They do not work for everyone, but do for many, if taken for long enough. For some sensitive people they work quite rapidly. A common experience is that people say "I'm not sure they help at all, but various things have changed in my life…" (What's more, other people often notice the change before we do ourselves). Flower essences are certainly not a universal panacea, but they can help many people to move forwards in life. A friend said they work by reflecting our self back to ourselves– and another said "You don't have to feel unwell to want to be better". Flower essences are tools to help us develop, mature and transform ourselves.

A personal example: Some years ago I knew intuitively that I had to take a Bach Flower Remedy called Larch. Larch helps with loss or lack of confidence. Now, I had no problems with confidence at the time - but I took it all the same. After two weeks, I found myself going swimming, something I had always avoided. As I swam up and down the pool, I reflected that I had learnt to swim aged nine, cold and unconfident and that this lack of confidence had tainted my attitude to swimming for thirty years! This was healed in two weeks by inexpensive support! What other hang-ups do we each carry, hidden and unresolved?

How to Choose and Use

Choosing essences is the difficult bit. There are helpful websites[3] and leaflets, such as and the Healing Herbs pocket prescriber[4]. It's often easy to look down a list and choose for someone else but more difficult for yourself. Sometimes just the process of reading about a flower remedy picture can give us intriguing insights into the psychology of personal development. Luckily, there are combinations available now to help us. Important combinations in UK are available from Neal's Yard (Bach Flower Essence Blends such as Courage, Direction, Letting Go, Optimism, Revitalise, SOS and Unwind), Balancing Blooms, (Cheer Up, Calm Down, Peace, Confidence and others), Jan de Vries range (Confidence, Mood, Night, Vitality and others), as well as the Australian Bush and Bailey Combinations.

Taking a combination is very simple, either using a ready made one such as Rescue Remedy or from another maker, or making up your own dosage bottle. 3-6 drops of each essence of choice should be placed into a 30ml bottle of ¼ vodka or brandy (preservative) and the rest water. The bottle should be tapped firmly to mix the essences together. Just put drops into a small amount of water and sip, onto your wrists (and rub in like perfume) or onto your tongue several times a day. You can do this for up to several weeks (remember the bacterial separation distance - don't lick the dropper!). Side effects appear rare. Flower essences can be used safely alongside any prescribed medication or other treatments. They can also be used topically or as a spray. Side-effects are uncommon, but might include a headache, nausea, heartburn (from brandy) and very rarely in sensitive people a paradoxical short lived negative psychological effect, the precise mechanism which is, as yet, unexplained. It seems that such people need contact with nature more directly, rather than information from a bottle.

Flower essences such as Rescue, SOS, Five Flower, Crisis or Emergency can be taken short term, for minor upsets, shock, upset, bad news exam nerves and so on. Every house should have one of these just in case! Actually, there's enough bad news in the world to benefit from taking these frequently, or for a period of two weeks every so often. Some people on night shifts find the Vitality, Get Up and Go and other combinations helpful for the brain fag that goes with working nights.

For many people, flower essences become effortless support tools for personal development, when taken for longer periods, as they provide information from nature that nourishes our software being and helps our development.

Many of us are sensitive to other peoples' emotions. We pick up on them easily and feel the hurt, especially if someone is upset or angry with us. Bach Walnut, Red Chestnut, Heather and Chestnut Bud act to protect most of us who are sensitive from this outside clutter, whilst Crab Apple and Hornbeam clean out the 'yuck' that has crept in! Yarrow (not one of Dr Bach's 38) is also protective.

Holly and Willow are good to allow more love into your life, especially if there's someone or something you feel less than loving towards! Calm Down contains these, and a number of people take it regularly, as it makes them feel better about life. It is also a good combination to help relieve work stress. The essences for sadness include Gentian, Gorse, Mustard and Sweet Chestnut, found in Optimism, Cheer Up and Mood Essence. These will help to lift our spirits when they are down. Wild Oat helps us find our true path; Scleranthus and Cerato also help this (all are in the Direction combination).

What's happens Whilst Using a Flower Essence?

Whilst taking the essences, many people notice not only a change for the present, but also old forgotten memories come to mind but in more positive light. During and after taking these combinations you may notice profound changes in yourself. You may experience the shedding of long-repressed tears. A variety of emotions may be released from deep within you and come to the surface to be acknowledged and released as the emotional memory banks are cleansed and healed. The following is the best description I know of this process:

> "The suggestion of using Bach Flower Remedies to help me at first seemed novel and different. Although I agreed to give them a try, I was very sceptical. They had been around since the 1930's and were developed

by a physician with a Harley Street practice so why wasn't every doctor prescribing them? I liked the idea of trying to treat the real problem. To begin with the Remedies (Mustard and Walnut) did not seem to be having a noticeable effect. Then I began to notice that various events or occasions in my life would come to mind. Often I would rethink these occasions, see what was really good in them for me and feel much more at ease with the thoughts.

"This happened not only to the good memories but to the bad ones as well. It was as if someone had opened the emotional filing cabinet and no way could I close it. Gradually I have found incident after incident coming to mind for reassessment, memories which at one time I could never have faced again, memories which I could not under any circumstances have shared with anyone could be dealt with and put away. Pandora's box of personal memories was revealing the bad things and gradually each was being cleaned away. In this process I learned to really cry again and not to withhold my feelings and batten them down. As a child my mother had insisted that my father never saw me in tears, but now the tears could flow freely. There was no guilt feeling about crying now. As the gentle cleansing and healing process has gone on over the weeks I have begun to realise that I am still an attractive woman with a lot to contribute to the world I live in.

"The whole effect seems to me to be rather like an old Dutch master's portrait which has become grimy and soiled with time and smoke from the fire. When it is gently cleaned and restored with modern techniques the beauty of the picture is almost better than in its original state; the lights and tones shine through much more clearly, the subtle hues and highlights become more apparent."

Lady, aged 53, Dec 97 having taken Mustard and Walnut for six weeks.

Personal Development – Experiences in the Workplace

As we move forwards in the 21st century, and positive psychology and mindfulness become common practices, flower and vibrational essences are powerful tools to help us develop and mature, and enhance our qualities of being. They assist us to 'unlearn' patterns of imbalance. Flower essences are now made around the world, from the UK (over 50 makers), to USA, South America, Australia, New Zealand, Tasmania, South Africa, Europe, Alaska, Africa and many other places.

In Brazil, Management Consultant Gustavo Boog has used this approach successfully in major corporations for over 20 years (author of 20 books including Energize Sua Empresa[5]). In Somerset they are used in the work setting with results that include: “my friend said how much more positive I am”; “marvellous - I feel so much better and things around me are too”; “thankyou, I feel stronger when taking them, so may I have some more?” There was also a big smile from one person who had been feeling overwhelmed (he had taken Calm Down for a couple of weeks). A monthly drop-in service was offered monthly to all staff in one NHS organisation during 2016-7. Over 70 attended the drop in service, with a number of regular users. Although some people have found no benefit, or did not persist with taking their combination for more than a day or two (often several weeks of ‘retuning’ is necessary to support the unlearning of discordant patterns of thoughts/feelings in adults, usually less in children), what was surprising was how competently nearly everyone was able to choose combinations that they could resonate with. This was by using the educational material available, and their own intuition, despite never having used flower essences before. Bach and Spirit-in-Nature were the most popular, with the Bailey Combinations also being used. The most detailed is quoted in full, from a lady aged 35, fully aware of the power of essences used in personal development:

> “I have noticed a real benefit from taking this combination. Almost as soon as I start taking the combination I feel a change that I can only describe as a certain lightness - a letting go. I do find I need to take the combination mindfully - as that anchors me in the moment of taking it and allows me to explore how I feel at that moment in time. This allows me as I go along to notice the change. For some reason, I also know when I can stop. The method of choosing - which you have taught me - is amazingly simple and I never thought that it would be so good in picking out what I need. I have earlier this year started a course on Mindfulness which complements this perfectly. There are no adverse effects at all. I also feel that the benefit of this is that it links into the core, the actual issue, rather than treating a surface symptom”.

Personal note: Andrew came across Bach Flower essences in the early 1990s, when a grateful patient gave him a set. Since then he has used the Bach and many others both for himself and many others. They are not for any medical condition, but help support us on our journey in life. Andrew is currently Life President of the UK Practitioners’ association, the BFVEA, and teaches health professionals and others about them for personal use.

Further resources can be found in the appendix.[6]

Centaury CC Andrew Tresidder

Honeysuckle CC Andrew Tresidder

Holly © Julian Barnard

Walnut © Julian Barnard

Red Chestnut © Julian Barnard

Heather CC Breathe Brandworks

These are models to help us understand the world of dealing with challenges and with what we know and don't know. They can help us make sense of our learning or of the work environment.

Urgent and Important

	Urgent	Not Urgent
Important	**1. Activities:** • Crises • Pressing problems • Deadline-driven projects	**2. Activities:** • Prevention • Preservation and maintenance activities • Relationship building • Recognising new opportunities • Planning • Recreation
Not Important	**3. Activities:** • Interruptions • Some calls • Some mail • Some reports • Some meetings • Proximate, pressing matters • Popular activities	**4. Activities:** • Trivia • Some mail • Some phone calls • Time wasters • Pleasant activities

The two factors that define an activity are **urgent** and **important**.

Urgent means it requires immediate attention - urgent matters are usually visible. They press on us; they insist on action.

Important on the other hand has to do with results. If something is important, it contributes to your mission, your values, and your high priority goals.

Quadrant 1 is both urgent and important. It deals with significant results that require immediate attention. We usually call the activities in quadrant 1 'crises' or 'problems'. We all have some quadrant 1 activities in our lives. But quadrant 1 consumes many people. They are crisis managers, problem-minded people, and deadline-driven producers. Some people are literally beaten up by problems all day every day. The only relief they have is in escaping to the not important, not urgent activities on quadrant 4. So when you look at their total matrix, 90% of their time is in Quadrant 1 and most of the remaining 10% is in Quadrant 4, with only negligible attention paid to Quadrants 2 and 3. That's how people who manage their lives by crises live.

There are other people who spend a great deal of time in urgent, but not important quadrant 3, thinking they are in quadrant 2. They spend most of their time reacting to things that are urgent, assuming they are also important. But the reality is that the urgency of these matters is often based on the priorities and expectations of others.

People who spend time almost exclusively in quadrants 3 and 4 basically lead irresponsible lives.

Effective people stay out of quadrants 3 and 4 because, urgent or not, they aren't important. They also shrink quadrant 1 down to size by spending more time in quadrant 2. Quadrant 2 is the heart of effective personal management. It deals with things that are not urgent, but are important. It deals with things like relationship building, long-range planning, exercising, preventative maintenance, and preparation - all those things we know we need to do, but seldom get around to doing, because they aren't urgent.

	Urgent	Not Urgent
Important	**1. Results:** • Stress • Burnout • Crises management • Always putting out fires	**2. Results:** • Vision • Perspective • Balance • Discipline • Control • Few crises
Not Important	**3. Results:** • Short-term focus • Crises management • Reputation - chameleon character • See goals and plans as worthless • Feel victimised, out of control • Shallow, or broken relationships	**4. Results:** • Total irresponsibility • Fired from jobs • Dependant on others or institutions for basics

Taken from The 7 Habits of Highly Effective People[1]

The Seven Habits of Highly Effective People may be of interest, as proven successful approaches in business and other organizations:

Stephen Covey's Seven Habits of Highly Effective People (over 15 million copies in print...) explores the fact that two people see an issue in different ways, and that if we work together, we can achieve far more. Progression involves a move from independence to Interdependence, and finally remembering to rest, repair and renew resources

The main points are:

1. **Be Proactive in life**, relationships, etc. Be positive. When asked something, have a 'can do' attitude.
2. **Begin with the End in Mind**. Be clear about your goal, think upon and develop your vision - not just for major goals, but day-to-day.
3. **Put First Things First.** Which includes looking after your own self - and your own health.
4. **Think Win-Win.** Move away from competition to cooperation. Valuing the other person and their point of view and respect are powerful tools.
5. **Seek First to Understand, then Be Understood.** Effective communication involves active listening, and careful attention to the other person.
6. **Synergize.** Using the power of the team can create outcomes no individual could ever achieve alone.
7. **Sharpen the Saw.** Spend time to renew your resources, health and energy. You may use exercise, quiet times, mindfulness, and of course good quality sleep and nutrition.

This common sense applied can help many of us in our lives.

Remember that, at any one point in life, there is only **one** single most important thing that you can being doing (not the same as the most urgent).

The **Johari Window** was created by **Jo**seph Luft and **Ha**rry Ingham in 1955.

It describes areas of our knowing.

A. **Open Window**. In this area is everything that is known to you and others.
B. **Blind Window**. In this box is everything that others can see about you that you cannot see yourself.
C. **Hidden Window**. In this box is everything we know about ourselves that we do not reveal to others.
D. **Unknown Window**. In this box is included feelings, thoughts and motives within you that are not known to you or others.

By sharing details of ourselves and receiving feedback from others we are able to increase our self knowledge and ensure that others know our 'true' selves. [Thanks to Suzanne Payne for this explanation.]

A. **Open**	B. **Blind**
(known to us and others) Behaviour Attitude Feelings Views Emotions Knowledge Skills	(unknown to us but known to others) Ignorance about oneself Delusion Issues withheld by others
C. **Hidden** (known to us but not known to others) Sensitivities Fears Hidden agendas Manipulative intentions Secrets	D. **Unknown** (not known to us or others) Feelings Latent abilities Aptitudes Experiences

Reflection points:

- Is there something that you would like others to better understand about you?
- How much of your hidden box would you choose to share with others?
- What type of environment makes this easier?
- Does your matrix differ between work and personal life?
- Consider the sizes of a child's boxes
- What are the key points in our lives that change the box sizes?
- How much time do you spend in the urgent quadrant 1?
- Do you ever spend time in the Important but non-urgent quadrant?
- How much time?

For scientists who have not studied economics, this brief guide may help.

Consumption

Consumption is the using up of resources for immediate needs. Whilst fulfilling immediate needs, this means that this resource is not available to use again. An example of excessive consumption is the purchase of more food than you need and throwing some away - or the purchase of a very expensive single meal, which spends all of your food budget for two or three days.

Savings

Delaying consumption allows the saving of resources – one example is the saving up of pocket money towards something we want.

Investment

Savings from the postponing of consumption allows the resources to be used to make something for future benefit and useful return. One example is saving some of your pay, putting it in the bank, gaining interest and then, in the future perhaps, buying a property. When you buy a property, you can then save paying rent, or rent it out to someone else. This is 'return on capital'. Another example is to install a cooker into a kitchen to allow hot food as well as cold to be produced.

Opportunity Cost

This important concept states that you can only do one thing at a time or that you can only use money or resources once. So if you spend a budget on one thing or purpose, then you can't spend it on another. Or if you take time to do X, then you may not have time to do Y. The implication of this is that with limited resources, such as our own time, we have to use it wisely and most effectively, not squander it. We should certainly make sure we cover what is important as well as what is urgent.

Law of diminishing returns

This states that beyond a certain point, you get less and less return for the same amount of investment. For example, it may be effective to spend three hours on paperwork, say, but the fourth hour may not achieve as much as hours one and two. Moreover, the seventh consecutive one certainly won't. (Again, a reason for using resources wisely.)

Supply and Demand
This classic economic model shows how price is fixed by the equilibrium between supply and demand. High supply with low demand brings a low price, whilst short supply with high demand will result in a higher price. So sometimes, agency staff may be very expensive.

Pharmaceutical medicines, whilst in patent, have a constricted supply and tend to keep a higher price. Then, when generics come in, supply increases and price usually drops. A monopoly supplier can impose price rises.

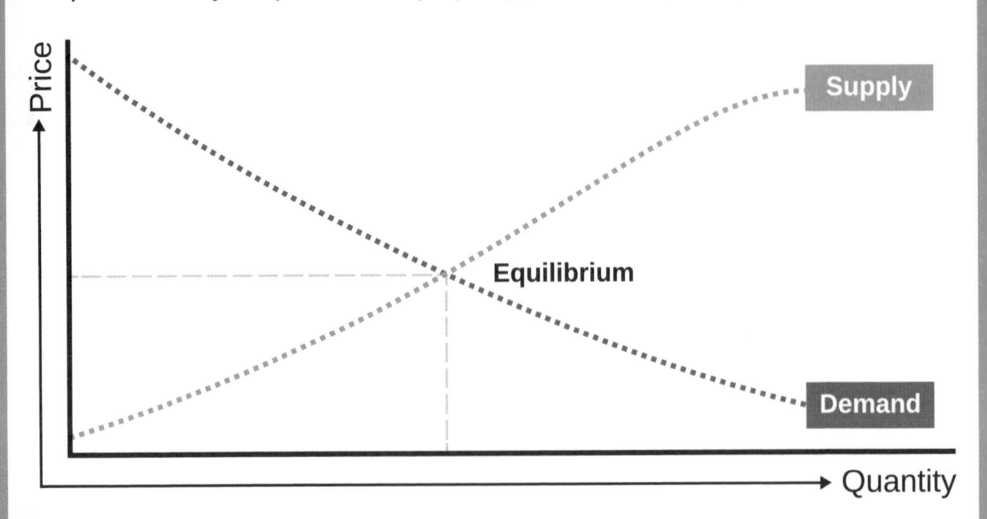

29.1 Supply and Demand

Marketing
However, despite the law of supply and demand, good marketing can buck the market trend. The classic story is sparkling perry (pear cider), which just didn't sell. They doubled the price, halved the size of the bottle and called it Babycham - which was a huge success in the 1960s.

The trouble with marketing is that 98% of marketing aims to make us feel dissatisfied with what we already have. The challenge of course is to work out which is the 2% that is worth our attention. Also, much of marketing is fear-based, envy-based, appeals to our prejudices, appeals to our desires (hunger, sweet taste, drink, sexuality, warmth, shelter, comfort) or otherwise seeks to distort our decision-making into fulfilling the marketer's needs rather than our own. What most marketing doesn't do is honestly give us information free from bias. We ourselves have to strip away that bias to make a wise decision for ourselves. Intuition Rules - but we have to listen to it!

Utility

Utility is the usefulness of something, or the benefit of an intervention. Marginal utility is the measurement of how much extra usefulness is obtained from another input of effort. Thus the repair of an uncomplicated hernia in a small child has much more utility than a similar repair on a bed-bound 98 year old (ethics seems to be creeping in here…) This might lead us into the thorny area of 'lives saved'. This is an emotional statement because at one level, no life is ever saved - though death can be postponed! Thus giving antibiotics to a small child with meningitis has a great utility (another 60 - 80 years of worthwhile life obtained for little cost), the resuscitation of a bed-bound 90 year-old with end-stage heart failure has little utility, though may perhaps have great ethical importance. (see Malcolm Kendrick's Doctoring Data - a great read to discover some biases and distortions within 'evidenced based medicine')

Prevention or Cure

The law here is that prevention is often unglamorous, low profile and upstream. It often attracts no attention (and may be neglected). Such an intervention might be like putting a fence at the top of a cliff.

Treatment and cure, however, is often more immediate, more glamorous, high profile and draws attention - such as lots of ambulances at the bottom of the cliff and shiny new hospitals with excellent trauma facilities. The irony of course is that installing a fence may reduce the need for the downstream (bottom of cliff) activity. But...

Both of course are important, nevertheless, the justification for prevention comes from the airline industry, where they say "safety may be expensive, but consider the cost of a mid-air collision."

Reflection points:

- What do you understand by 'supply and demand'? How might it apply in your life?
- What is the difference between consumption and investment?
- Have you ever noticed diminishing returns during your work day?

Compassion (see also section 4, pp11-13)
The Dalai Lama described compassion as *"a sensitivity to the suffering of self and others, with a deep commitment to relieve it"*. The Latin derivation means fellow-suffering. Anthony William states:

"Compassion is the understanding of suffering. There is no peace, joy or hope until those who suffer are understood. Compassion is the soul of these words; without it, they are empty. Compassion fills them with truth, honour and purpose".

Compassion is: Treating someone as you would wish to be treated… listening without judging... and doing your best in every interaction.

Compassionate care has been described as "attention in life and living to the giving of understanding, support, advice, care and reassurance that helps foster health and wellbeing"[1] . Dr Paquita de Zulueta[2], a London GP describes four key components of being compassionate:

1. Awareness of and resonance with the suffering of another (emotional empathy).
2. Correct perspective towards this person (cognitive empathy).
3. Distress tolerance (can manage the emotional situation safely). An aspect of resilience.
4. Motivation to act and relieve the suffering.

Compassionate practice in healthcare increases patient and staff satisfaction, and results in improved diagnosis, improved outcomes, fewer errors and complaints.

Emotions
Biologically there are three mammalian emotional systems:

1. **Drive**; to motivate us towards resources, with feelings of wanting, pursuing, achieving, progressing and focused (dopamine dominant).
2. **Soothing**; affiliative, with feelings of contentment, safety and connection (opiate and oxytocin) - related to the parasympathetic nervous system.
3. **Threat**; safety-seeking, threat-focused, with feelings of anger, anxiety and disgust (adrenaline dominant) - related to the sympathetic nervous system.

The second of these is deeply involved in nurture and compassion and is integral to the nature of a human being. It both requires and gives rise to secure attachments and results in emotional maturity of the limbic system. It is both a masculine and a feminine aspect, but also deeply relates to the role of mother and maternal care and support.

Unfortunately sympathetic drive (fear, fight and flight) shuts down the parasympathetic system; and even worse, it shuts down our frontal cortex activity in the brain and prevents us from thinking rationally. So, it not only stops us being able to rationalize, but also to nurture.

An environment with fear as a dominant emotion erodes compassion. Paquita argues strongly for developing compassionate leadership in healthcare, and argues that recent NHS changes and target driven culture diminish the ability for leaders to set a culture of compassion.

Compassion is a two way process: in energetic terms there is a connection which results in an energy flow of love towards the person you are being compassionate to and in a connection of the compassionate person to a deeper aspect of humanity and a wellspring of love. Compassion is a win-win situation - as long as it includes self-compassion.

Kindness, support and love towards another *through* your 'self' has positive benefits for giver and receiver. It allows us to be energised and refreshed by a flow of love and kindness that has its source beyond us, in a higher dimension. It should include self-compassion. If it doesn't, the compassion is coupled with self-denial or martyrdom, which can be exhausting and is unsustainable.

If we are kind to ourselves, allow ourselves to be present, and to have an 'inner smile', then we can feel well in ourselves. We can also function well, perform well, and be compassionate with ease. If in addition we allow ourselves mindfully to observe the present moment in a non-judgmental fashion and remember to be grateful for each moment of life, then we are a long way towards inner refreshment and effortless ability to be compassionate to self and others.

Mindfulness is a powerful tool to remind us to be 'human beings', not just 'human doings. Mindfulness helps us re-member (remember) who we are, by the practice of loving acceptance of our experience of each present moment as it arises.

Robin Philipp summarises 'self-compassion' as:

"Taking care to ensure that as well as caring for others we care for ourselves". *"It's about being kind to ourselves, giving ourselves time and treating*

ourselves with love, care, dignity and self-respect. It's also about being in the present moment, accepting and non-judgmental when encountering pain and personal shortcomings, and accepting of these feelings. This requires taking a balanced approach to one's negative emotions so that feelings are neither accepted nor exaggerated. Instead it's about observing them within and with openness so that they are held in 'mindful awareness'; a non-judgmental, receptive state in which individuals observe their thoughts and feelings as they are without trying to suppress or deny them. Properly learned and applied it can be an effective tool to reduce stress and enhance one's wellbeing".[1]

Of course, living this isn't quite so easy since hurt on the inside on any issue, from present, past, childhood, or from family, tribal, racial or other prejudices, can lead to us hitting out! But if we heal our own hurts, then it is very difficult to hit out. So, it's worth working on ourselves because as we heal our hurts, develop ourselves, and achieve greater maturity and wisdom, compassion flows ever more easily.

As we work on ourselves, we remember (*re*-member) the human condition that we all share: its frailty, vulnerability, errors and fallibility and we honour and respect it. We love it just how it is, for what it is. We become kind to others as we become kinder to ourselves. We mature in love, in self-respect, in standing comfortably in our own skins and being true to our 'selves'. We love our 'selves' for who we are - we release any self-judgment, thoughts of self-harm in thought, word or deed, self-pity and self-indulgence. We become wiser and kinder. We become mindful of who we are, and stiller in our 'selves'.

From inner love and inner strength, compassion flows easily, even effortlessly, as we develop ourselves in this way. If we feel valued and even thanked, then the flow of compassion is ever easier.

An attitude of gratitude makes the world go round.

Compassionate environments

Compassion can be a tender flower; it needs a supportive environment to flourish. A critical judgmental environment will handicap peoples' ability to be compassionate.

De Zulueta writes that Compassionate care requires a Compassionate Culture:

- A high-trust nurturing environment, which breeds security.
- Characterized by compassionate 'soft power' leadership.
- Exists within a values driven organization.

- Enables good teams and good relationships.
- Provides support, both informal and professional (such as supervision).
- Designs a workload within - not exceeding capabilities (ie not overwhelming).
- Allows time to care.
- Implements organizational wellness strategies.
- Provides reflective spaces, reflective people, reflective groups (Schwartz Rounds and Balint Groups help this)
- Fosters the nurturing of self-care and autonomy.

Anna Baverstock and Fiona Finlay[3] suggest developing your own compassion toolkit, so that you can nurture your self on a regular basis - akin to topping up the fuel tank of love and support.

By connecting with nature, we are refreshed - images of landscapes, the sea, water or sky can be supportive. Likewise, the rhythm and patterns of poetry, music, art and exercise, hobbies, play with others or alone - anything which engages us in Flow in Life, and which connects us to Flow, and which feeds and nurtures our need for connection to harmonious patterns in life - helps us forwards on our journey. Surely part of that journey is to nourish compassion, especially in the caring professions.

To help us develop character and qualities: tuning forks such as Bach and other flower essences can be valuable. When we connect deeply with nature, we discover our own inner nature and retune the soul.

As they say, love makes the world go round - and also, what goes around, comes around - you reap as you sow…

Never underestimate the potential of repeated small acts of kindness to help transform the world - as we transform our 'selves'…

Who cares for the carers if they do not care for themselves?

One model of success involves MAP - Mastery, Autonomy and Purpose[4]. It is found that people who take on these concepts, and those organizations that support this, do well. So when a person:

1. Has purpose they are clear about what they want to achieve
2. Has mastery they master the skills they need and they master themselves.
3. Has autonomy they have a degree of ability to manage and direct themselves, within the needs of the organization.

That person does well and feels good and so does the organization.

An organization that invests in staff training and staff well-being is always more effective and sustainable than one that does not.

Top Tips for Team Working for New Consultants (and all doctors)

Number One Rule: try to treat others as you would wish to be treated yourself…

From a former director of nursing:

1. Cultivate good relationships with senior nurses; maintain and develop these.
2. Manage your patients' expectations from day one.
3. Always be honest with your patients and relatives.
4. Patients will not always hear - or remember - what is said; try to have a relative or friend there to help them and copy them in on correspondence. Use advice leaflets; communicate as effectively as possible.
5. Take ownership of your cases - keep the person alive in your mind
6. Do no harm! You may wish to use The Surgeon's Checklist[1].

From senior nurse managers:

1. Communicate well, smile often and take a team approach.
2. Nobody likes a 'primadonna', though senior roles can be lonely.
3. Avoid aggression - it demonstrates insensitivity or distress.
4. Acknowledge expertise and know where to find information from colleagues.
5. Acknowledge your juniors; they may have more knowledge about specific issues.
6. Seek to empower others; successful outcomes are a team effort.
7. If you're at an arrest, let the F2 (or at least the best person) lead.
8. Be yourself and build relationships not isolation.
9. Vulnerability is NOT weakness.
10. Most people are good - some excellent - at detecting truth deficiency. Beware!
11. Be respectful to everyone at all levels that you work with; status is only a temporary phenomenon.
12. Engage in teaching - juniors really appreciate this.
13. If you are not sure, ask. Engage with the senior nurse team.

From current consultants:

1. Make sure you introduce yourself to everyone you need to meet and keep a notebook with names (unless you have a photographic memory).
2. Meet all your ward sisters and share with them what you want to achieve.
3. Try to attend any social or other introductory meetings - they will help you make lasting and supportive relationships.
4. In your first year, don't necessarily say 'yes' to everything but don't have a blanket 'no' either.

5. Get the basics right from day one: ward rounds, outpatients, operating, departmental meetings and so on, without necessarily taking on lots of other commitments.
6. Make allies with integrity and learn the logistics of who's who and where things are.
7. There is a difference between confidence and overconfidence; most people can usually tell.
8. Go and meet each department and service you interact with - a personal contact goes a very long way and is always appreciated.
9. Many doctors worry about the bad (news or outcomes) and don't hear the good. Perfectionism can be destructive, so avoid falling into this trap.
10. People remember first impressions. (A friendly smile, even if you feel nervous; clean shoes; tidiness).
11. Be mindful of outcomes - remember not to react too quickly: stimulus; PAUSE; consider; respond!
12. The response "how can I help?" is a better one than "why should I?"
13. Being a consultant is not a mandate for raising your voice.
14. Learn to watch other peoples' body language.
15. Act with integrity.
16. Build a good relationship with senior nurses and ward sisters.
17. Feel confident in your own ability.
18. Addiction to being busy doing things stops people reflecting…
19. Be yourself, don't try to live up to other peoples' ideals or expectations and avoid posturing. People will cut you some slack for the first 18 months. Use this time wisely to invest in relationships and skill-sets
20. Teach juniors - they really appreciate it.
21. Under pressure, some people resort to playground behaviour - you may wish to avoid this trap…
22. Go to the canteen and meet colleagues to eat together. If you find yourself eating alone in your office often, ask yourself whether you could/should be somewhere else!
23. Kindness goes a very long way and is always remembered.
24. People, like dogs, may need to mark lamp-posts - they need to feel safe in their territory.

From new consultants:

1. Have a clear vision for the future but be prepared to negotiate and be patient.
2. Learn presentation skills.
3. Be honest and show your integrity and it will reward you many times over.
4. Work out who to go to if there is trouble or upset, before it occurs.
5. Make friends and allies; discover who feels threatened.

6. Seek always to understand first before trying to be understood.
7. Leadership can be either overt, subtle, or both.
8. Take advantage of any leadership training offered.
9. Offer to teach - it is always appreciated.
10. Keep your perspective.
11. Take time to reflect daily. Appreciate and be grateful for what goes well.
12. Share lessons with colleagues to avoid reinventing the wheel.

Common Fantasies, Fears and Misconceptions
(You may choose to release and grow beyond them).

1. That the buck stops with you - because there are always colleagues to support. You may have the expertise; others have had similar experiences.
2. Being good, or looking good, can only be at someone else's expense (FALSE!)
3. That you are invincible (you're not).
4. That you are always right (you're not).
5. That you are alone (you're not).
6. That your own health needs no attention (FALSE!).
7. That the Drama Triangle does not apply to you (learn about it!).
8. That you cannot learn from feedback (FALSE!).
9. That adults don't suffer from shame, guilt, fear, worries or upset (they can and do).
10. That you know everything (we never stop learning in life).
11. That an angry man is a bully (he might be, but actually distress often betrays itself as anger or frustration, especially in a male).

What's most important for a successful long-term career?
In a nutshell: settle down, avoid over-commitment, gain confidence in your basics (process of ward-rounds, clinics; relationships; the hospital; the hierarchy) - and avoid making much noise for the first year!

1. Know yourself (and be yourself - every one else is taken…).
2. Avoid burnout (and avoid burning bridges) - learn about thriving with pressure and challenges (there is often a honeymoon period after which there can be a bit of gloom - if so, talk to your mentor).
3. Grow beyond being a 'little pleaser' or a 'little rebel'.
4. Remember support nurtures and helps people blossom and flourish - criticism can wither. Being too much of a personal perfectionist may manifest as criticism of others - beware of this trap.
5. Follow your passion to be great at what you do.
6. Take time to nurture yourself outside work.

7. Take time to nurture relationships at work - informal culture is just as important at winning hearts as formal methods are at winning minds.
8. Keep a 'gratitude diary' - write down 5 things at the end of each day you are grateful for so that at the end of a month you have 150 in the bank!
9. Find reasons to be positive.
10. Remember that, in life, we can learn something from each person we meet and each circumstance we engage in.
11. Learn about the Seven Habits of Highly Effective People.[2]
12. Follow your dreams (where do you see yourself and your department in five years?) and keep a lively interest in life and other people.
13. Make lists - aspirations, expectations, relationships, networks, roles…
14. If you find yourself feeling down, unhappy, upset, frustrated or hurt, find a trusted colleague to help you reflect and analyse why - the weather is not the same as the landscape and you may need help to diagnose and analyse the issue. Don't walk alone; seek help, and stop experiencing the same frustrating weather… Help is there if you wish.
15. Try and keep a clear desk and deal with a piece of paper only once.
16. Tell your secretary how you want to work your filing system. Work with her/him rather than expecting them to just do it.
17. Get to know your GP colleagues; meet them if possible and trust that they will do right for the patients.
18. Admin have all their own pressures - work with them and understand these - not against them!
19. Avoid tribalism (them and us).
20. Be loyal to your organisation.
21. Don't be flattered by being asked…
22. Remember, many doctors have traits of perfectionism, self-criticism, or can catastrophise. If you find yourself doing this - or being narcissistic - then you have lost perspective and need support to regain it.
23. Make sure you have your own GP.
24. Patients may forget what you say, but they always remember how you make them feel.

Suggested Organisational Supports

1. Induction
2. Welcome meeting
3. Consider welcome dinners / informal events for senior staff. It sets a great example of leadership.
4. Help new key staff make outside relations (for example: consultants with GPs).
5. Suggest each new intake of junior staff (doctors etc) has a specific welcome

meeting / fun event - this can weld a department together powerfully for teamwork.

6. Ensure there is good teaching and educational events which are specialty / grade specific.
7. Consider emotional wellbeing training as part of optional or mandatory training.
8. Consider self knowledge (such as a team completing Myers-Briggs assessments) or Chimp Training (The Chimp Paradox, Prof Steve Peters) as a valuable investment for the future.
9. Leadership skills for middle grades as well as seniors.
10. Arrange a mentor for all new staff.
11. Observing other's practice (for example: ward rounds, clinic and so on).
12. Consider rehearsing a 'dummy clinic' in the first week just to make sure all works well, all equipment is present, staff all know each other and so on. The 'patients' could be made up of staff, each coming to meet and share for a few minutes, maybe including support staff such as those from radiology , the pathology lab and other services.
13. Support all (especially small) specialities in making external professional relationships - including hosting single discipline or themed educational activities.
14. Follow up with constructive feedback at appropriate times, especially for new staff.

Example: one new junior doctor, three months into the job, was asked in the lift (to his surprise and complete pleasure) by a senior consultant how he was getting on – this made his day and left a warm glow for some time... (It was still remembered some thirty years later).

Common scenarios to expect in the first year

(Remember, this is Life just testing you and trying you out on some simple and sometimes more complicated issues in order for you to learn more):

1. An arrest/ faint/ anaphylactic shock/hypoglycaemic attack in clinic (probably in a patient, but might be staff!)
2. An angry patient.
3. A distressed member of staff.
4. An issue of conflict.
5. A complaint.
6. Lots of successes!

1a Health is harmony of mind, body and spirit. We all feel better when we are feeling well! Trite perhaps, but still very true. The opposite was recently voiced "Feeling miserable doesn't half get you down, doesn't it?" Furthermore, you don't have to feel unwell to want to get better. People who feel valued and connected to a personal purpose, philosophy and faith in life, and who feel connected to the wonder and energy of our natural world, feel well. People who breathe calmly, rhythmically and mindfully with gratitude, feel happy. People who breathe chaotically, selfishly and ungratefully, often feel stressed and unhappy.

1b Unfortunately, unless as individuals we happen to be well already, for many, feeling well seems to be a matter of luck. However, emotional health is a state of well-being that can be attained by each of us, using a personal health strategy. In fact, one of the major barriers to emotional well-being is the attitude of "I'm fine, I don't need any help". This attitude reflects the denial mechanism that we all use from time to time to help us deal with our own very personal emotional broken glass. Health professionals often use displacement ("I'm too busy with my patients") as well as denial. Hence many of us avoid making deposits into the Bank of Health.

1c A **pro-active personal, corporate and community-wide health strategy** can dramatically affect the well-being of many people, both in the workplace and in society at large.

1d Psychological imbalance will coexist with many physical illnesses, as well cause mental health problems in later life. Some people live with unhappiness or misery, and may be tempted to give away their power (or money) to find external answers. "You're well until you're ill then see the Doctor for a pill…" (or buy a substance, or have a drink (alcohol or sugary)) seems to be a modern mantra for some people, though the great majority of people actually take much more responsibility for themselves than these trite comments suggest. Yet life is actually a journey of personal development, from childhood on. We either learn skills and wisdom, and do well or we develop dysfunctional coping strategies and an unresolved accumulation of unresolved emotional hurts, which drag us into misery or inner hurt.

1e We then either internalise the inner hurts and drift into misery (which may become depression) or are paralysed by fear that manifests as anxiety. Alternatively, we palliate our emotional pains with outbursts (projection), alcohol/substance use (blot out), retail therapy or device addiction (distraction) or eating (comfort behaviour). A danger for society is that this issue becomes medicalised and palliated, not healed. (Of course, mental illness needs proper detection and treatment, however many people have the blues or unresolved loss without mental illness).

2a The **knowledge, skills and attitudes** needed to attain personal emotional well-being are not difficult to learn. Coping skills are already known to different extents and there is considerable scope for increasing their prevalence. New proactive skills are easily learnt, for instance emotion coaching in self-regulation for children. This applies equally to the 'child' inside many adults. The five steps of emotion coaching are logical: be *aware of emotions* (your own and others); *connect* with the other person; *listen* to the other person; *name* the emotions; *find* good solutions.[1]

3a The workplace can generate stress and distress, whilst more may come from home or elsewhere. Wherever it is generated, however, emotional distress impacts every other area of our lives. What matters in life is not what happens to us (the events) but how we react to them.

3b The cost of not dealing pro-actively to resolve pent-up emotional stress is seen widely in life. The after-effects range from frustration to anger, violence, alcoholic obliteration, to domestic violence and broken homes. Furthermore, they often subsequently reflect in the behaviour of children and partners.

3c Past litigation and recent good practice has supported employers to be pro-active in providing **emotional health strategies**. These may include re-organisation of the workplace to promote greater harmony, performance appraisal strategies, provision of emotional resilience workshops and counselling services and the like. Good working practices are already widespread and need only to be enhanced to cover the emotional component.

3d Modern understanding of emotional health has reached the point where it is worth agreeing and implementing an emotional health strategy to involve the whole workforce and society; not just to deal reactively with problems as they manifest, but to help individuals pro-actively to enhance their health and well-being. "You don't have to feel unwell to want to get better".

3e This will necessarily include **good communication, good management** and the teaching of **personal emotional healing skills** that we all can use by ourselves. Other facilities that may be used include, amongst others, **counselling, or support at crisis time** to deal with old or hidden issues (IAPT and society's skillsets, for example: Big White Wall, Samaritans, MIND and other agencies), NLP, complementary practitioner support and flower essence use on a personal basis - even where there are no current problems. The powerful personal techniques of mindfulness, acupressure for emotions,

Emotional Stress Release and EFT, the Emotional Freedom Technique, are also useful skills for us all to master and use personally. A recent pilot in the workplace of Flower Essences for Personal Development (used in Brazil for over 20 years, see section 27 (p154)) has shown interesting results.

4a An emotional health strategy: can we afford not to - either at work or for home life?

The tragic results of non-action are the partners who are ignored or abused, the children who are shouted at, the emptiness that many feel in their lives, and the collapse into alcoholic or TV induced obliteration that so many use. This is in addition to poor productivity, low morale and sickness absence. The positive potential is a society comprised of people with profound inner security and self-worth. They tend to say "How can I help?", "I can" and "Why shouldn't I?", rather than the "can'ts", "shan'ts" and "why should I's?" that we so often hear. A challenge for us all to rise to?

4b A progressive model of addiction recognises the importance of addiction as self-medication for pain - pain at either physical, psychological, social or spiritual (meaning and purpose of life) levels. Any approach that does not take into consideration all four levels is likely to fail in the long term.

5a We must remember that high quality sleep, freedom from electromagnetic pollution, freedom from chemical pollution including artificial sweeteners such as aspartame (metabolised to methanol and formaldehyde), freedom from neurotoxins and carcinogens, regular access to fresh air, sunlight, exercise, and regular consumption of nutritious (ideally locally grown) food, including fruit, vegetables, and appropriate amounts of good fats (avoiding overconsumption of refined carbohydrates) is also crucial to underpin good functioning of the brain and body. Principles from Ayurvedic medicine and modern nutritional medicine have much to offer.

5b The website www.canceractive.com has helpful advice on how to maintain health and for those in recovery from cancer, as well as excellent articles on orthodox approaches.

5c Health is also helped by personal practices such as yoga, tai chi, pilates, exercise, sport, dancing, and many other physical approaches, as well as appropriate structural or bodywork support from therapists (physio, osteopathy, aromatherapy, massage, Bowen technique among many others).

5d Our Emotional Health Strategy - be proactive!

33 Poem of Gratitude

Thank you to all contributors to this book for their great support, we hope it helps you on your journey.

We respect, love and honour the Life which flows equally through all facets of creation including each of us.

This Life Force supports all of creation, including all of nature, our planet earth, and all humans, equally and unconditionally.

Purpose guides the force to allow experiences to happen throughout creation. Everyday events are pregnant with meaning, often at many levels. As events unfold, we may perceive deeper patterns of meaning. From all of these we learn, and continue to learn.

We give thanks for the gift of life which allows us to awaken each day refreshed by blessed sleep, and which gives us another day of experiences and learning.

We give thanks for the warmth of the sun, and for the food from the earth, the water and the air that nourishes all life.

We recognise that life is a mirror - that if we withhold love from someone, it will be withheld from us, and if we block the flow and rhythm of life, it will be blocked for us in turn. On the other hand, we can allow love to flow effortlessly from an infinite source through each of us if we choose.

We give thanks and joy through our every waking moment, through work, song, dance, laughter, love, joy and all the things that we do. We give thanks for our wonderful bodies, which are our precious vehicles on this journey - we love them dearly!

We are helped to listen to the still small voice of truth within us, and to recognise and follow the inner knowing that connects directly to and is supported by Life. This way we avoid danger and temptations, as we follow the path of Life and stay true to the Love that surrounds us and guides us.

We feel nourished and supported from within - for we are content, and leave others free to be themselves. We release the need to plunder or steal energy from others, recognising that we can access an infinite source of love and energy from Life when we remember to.

For we each, and all, are part of Life, part of the great Dance of Life, and we all dance together. We truly appreciate Life.

And so be it for Eternity.

Anon

I am your friend and my love for you goes very deep. There is nothing I cannot give you which you have not already got, but there is much, very much, that, while I cannot give it, you can take. No heaven can come to us unless our hearts find rest in today. Take heaven! No peace lies in the future that is not hidden in this present little instant. Take peace! The gloom of the world is but a shadow. Behind it, yet within our reach, is joy! There is radiance and glory in the darkness could we but see… and to see we have to look. I beseech you to look!

Life is so generous a giver, but we, judging its gifts by the covering, cast them away as ugly, or heavy or hard. Remove the covering and beneath you will find a living splendour, woven of love, by wisdom, with power. Welcome it, grasp it, touch the angel's hand that brings it to you. Everything we call a trial, a sorrow, or a duty, believe me, that angel's hand is there, the gift is there, and the wonder of an overshadowing presence. Our joys, too, be not content with them as joys. They, too, conceal diviner gifts. Life is so full of meaning and purpose, so full of beauty - beneath its covering - that you will find earth but cloaks your heaven.

Courage, then, to claim it - that is all. But courage you have, and the knowledge that we are all pilgrims together, wending our way through unknown country, home. And so, at this time, I greet you. Not quite as the world sends greeting, but with profound esteem and with the prayer that for you now and forever, the day breaks and the shadows flee away.

Life is by invitation.

There are many levels of perception and meaning.

Love underpins everything in the universe.

Heaven and earth are not far from each other.

Let he who has eyes to see, see - and understand.

What's going on behind what's going on?

Take Peace.

From inner peace springs knowing and from knowing can come effective action.

Tota Vita Sacra Est.

Always try to see the other person's point of view.

Life, Love, Live

Exercise: role-play around the Drama Triangle. See sections 14 to 15. We suggest one person takes 'role A', and the other 'role B'. Please read the scripts, and then conduct a 'pretend' consultation for five minutes. When finished, the patient (B) MUST thank the person playing A and say what a good doctor they have just been.
This is a fictitious script. Please avoid becoming involved in any real case that you may know. Try and observe which 'roles' are being played and by whom. Next, stop the play, thank each other, and analyse what Drama Triangle Roles are played by whom.

A. Victim, Rescuer, Persecutor - (patient)

You are an obese man of 57 with a BMI of 35. Two years ago your knee gave you pain, and stopped you playing golf. Your family doctor gave you medication and advice, including weight loss. An X Ray showed mild osteoarthritis.

After six months you insisted on referral for surgery. Medication had not helped the pain (nor had you lost weight). A year ago you had a knee replacement, after the usual pre-op counselling.

Your knee is worse and you are in pain. You wish that you hadn't had the operation and are angry with your family doctor for referring you. You think of suing the surgeon. Today you have come to see your family doctor, and you want to 'let off steam'; to voice your anger.

B. Victim, Rescuer, Persecutor - (doctor)

Mr J is an obese 57 year old. Two years ago he consulted you. His knee gave him pain, though he continued to work. You advised strongly weight loss and gave analgesic medication. An X Ray showed only mild osteoarthritis.

After six months Mr J insisted on referral for surgery, as medication had not helped the pain. His weight was the same. You referred him with reluctance. A year ago he had a knee replacement.

Today he returns. The knee is worse and he has constant pain. He wishes that he had not had the operation and is angry with you for referring him. He asks whether he should sue the surgeon.

After five minutes, stop the role play. Thank your colleague. You are now a health professional again. Please discuss the issues with your colleague, and analyse the roles that are played.

Where is the role of Victim played? And by whom?
Where is the role of Persecutor played? And by whom?
Where is the role of Rescuer played? And by whom?
What role does the medical condition play? (Persecutor, victim or rescuer?)
Hint: see pp74-75.

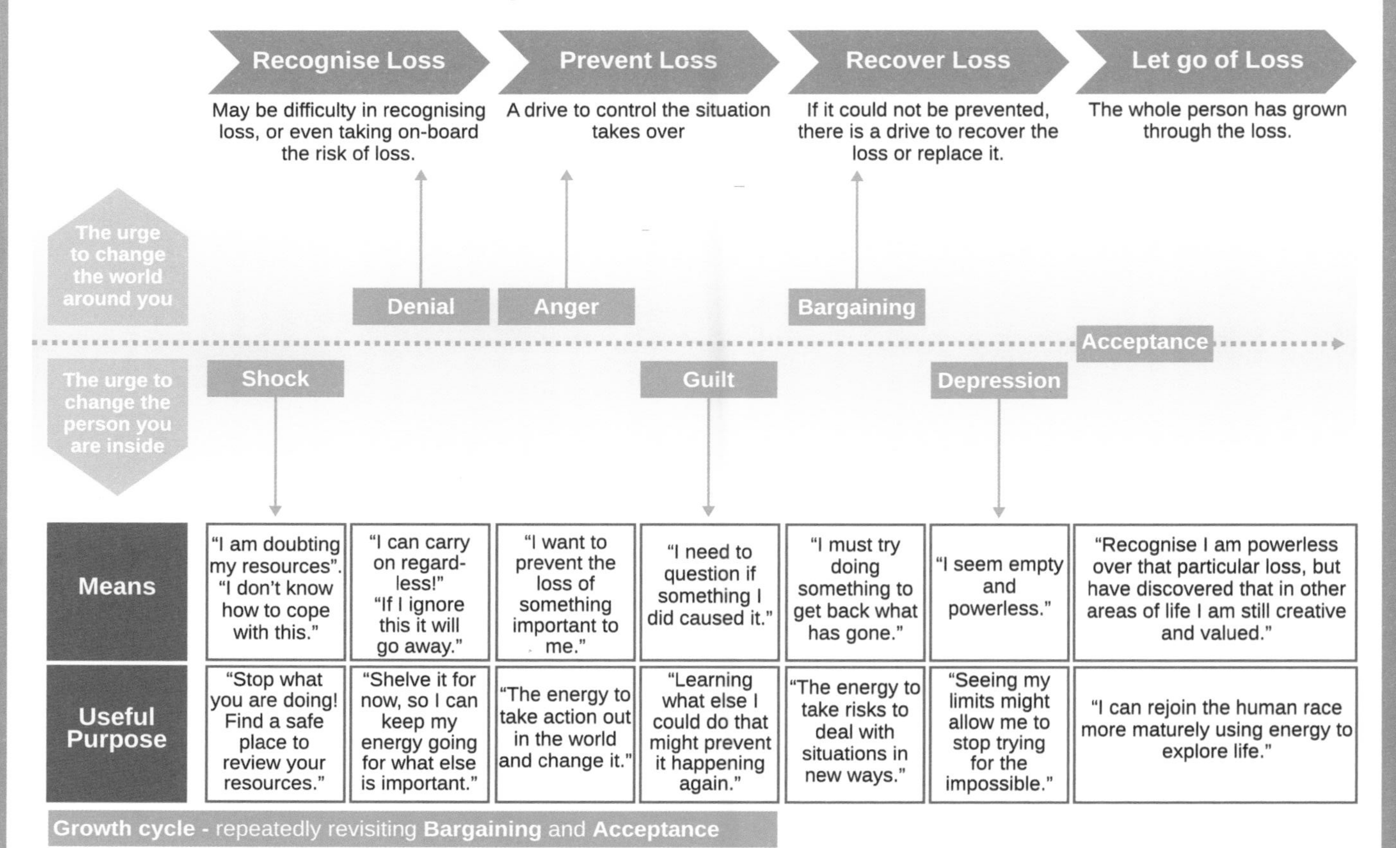
Turning Points as you Adjust to Change
Recognise Loss
May be difficulty in recognising loss, or even taking on-board the risk of loss.
Prevent Loss
A drive to control the situation takes over
Recover Loss
If it could not be prevented, there is a drive to recover the loss or replace it.
Let go of Loss
The whole person has grown through the loss.
The urge to change the world around you
Denial
Anger
Bargaining
Acceptance
The urge to change the person you are inside
Shock
Guilt
Depression
Means
"I am doubting my resources". "I don't know how to cope with this."
"I can carry on regard-less!" "If I ignore this it will go away."
"I want to prevent the loss of something important to me."
"I need to question if something I did caused it."
"I must try doing something to get back what has gone."
"I seem empty and powerless."
"Recognise I am powerless over that particular loss, but have discovered that in other areas of life I am still creative and valued."
Useful Purpose
"Stop what you are doing! Find a safe place to review your resources."
"Shelve it for now, so I can keep my energy going for what else is important."
"The energy to take action out in the world and change it."
"Learning what else I could do that might prevent it happening again."
"The energy to take risks to deal with situations in new ways."
"Seeing my limits might allow me to stop trying for the impossible."
"I can rejoin the human race more maturely using energy to explore life."
Growth cycle - repeatedly revisiting Bargaining and Acceptance
Health and Self-Care, Thanks to Alex Aylward with Acknowledgment to Emotional Logic Centre"

Suggestions for Light Medical and Leadership Reading.

The SafeMed Handbook, Dr Margaret O'Rourke. University of Cork, 2013. A superb text in coaching style which reminds us to take care of our body, our mind, our behaviour, the context we live in, and our spirit - one of the two best introductory books I have, Stop the Stress of Medicine being the other.

Stop the Stress of Medicine, Dr David Rainham. Canada's teacher on "Dr Stress", a Cardiff graduate and Ontario GP and long time teacher and lecturer on empowering yourself and taking control. Excellent volume, used by London's PHP for patients and widely in the UK to promote self-knowledge and resilience.

Stop Physician Burnout, Dr Dike Drummond. Along with Stop the Stress of Medicine, should be the prescribed texts for the subject of promoting physician resilence - a superb book that is both a resource and a coaching aid to help self.

The Naked Consultation, Dr Liz Moulton. Brilliant text for GP Trainers and all who wish to cover the soft curriculum of consultation skills - covers lots of psychology relevant to doctors, including visual auditory and kinaesthetic learners - if you don't know what these are, do read it - you are one of the three!

The Physician as Patient, Myers and Gabbard. American Psychiatric Association, 2008. *The* text on diagnosis and treatment of physicians with mental and behavioural disorders.

Coherence: The Secret Science of Brilliant Leadership, Dr Alan Watkins. 2014, Kogan Page, London and Philadelphia. Alan shares many models and concepts on health and leadership, including cardiac coherence - harmony brought about in the human system through coherent (not chaotic) breathing.

Games People Play, Eric Berne. 1964. (classic text on Transactional Analysis, required reading for every practitioner) together with the up to date story.

Counselling for Toads Robert de Board Routledge, a light hearted look at Therapy in practice, for the repentant Toad of Toad Hall, the racing car-driving swash-buckling hero of the children's classic Wind in the Willows.

The Four Agreements, Don Miguel Ruiz. South American wisdom about life.

The Fifth Agreement, Don Miguel Ruiz and Don Jose Ruiz

Developing Compassionate Leadership in Healthcare: an Integrative review, Paquita C de Zulueta http://bit.ly/HaSC001

Energy Medicine, James Oschman. Elsevier, 2015, 2nd Ed. Current biomedicine is based on Newtonian cause and effect, and a narrative of Chemistry to underpin pathology, physiology and therapeutics. It is based on chemistry for the hardware, and physics for the software. Humans are actually beings of information as well as blood, bones, pipes and pumps. Oschman explores the vital importance of this, and implications for medicine and health.

Leading out of Who You Are, Simon P Walker. In the first of the Leadership Trilogy, Simon, a former priest, looks at personal factors including 'front stage and back stage' of who we are, and how we can use our power wisely, giving worked examples of historical figures.

The Holistic Doctor, Dr Deborah McManners. A British GP, Deborah is also a naturopath, aiming to support the body to health itself by helping provide the right conditions for health. Excellent thoughts on food tolerance, nutrition in general, and chemical and environmental pollution that affects our health.

The Biology of Belief, Dr Bruce Lipton. Be prepared to learn that genes are not static, and that our thoughts affect our biology far more than we would wish to believe… Thorough treatment of the subject, should be read by all students of science.

The Cosmic Hologram, Jude Currivan. Information at the Centre of the Universe from a Physicist and scientist.

Prevent and Cure Diabetes, Dr Sarah Myhill and Craig Robinson. One of the few doctors who understands nutrition at a deep level, and who treats top athletes for CFS/ME - see also her book Diagnosis and Treatment of Chronic Fatigue Syndrome and Myalgic Encephalitis - it's mitochondria, not hypochondria.

The Enlightened Gardener, Sydney Banks. Interesting take on how the world works - with Universal Thought, Mind and Consciousness the three guiding principles.

Everything You Need to Know to Help You Beat Cancer, Chris Woollams and www.canceractive.com. Evidence based wisdom to help with a pervasive modern illness, with both orthodox and nutritional approaches critiqued.

Anti-Cancer, Dr David Servan-Schreiber. A story as to how one physician adopted approaches to help stay healthy - after being given a two year prognosis for a brain tumour, he exceed this by another fifteen years, by studying why some people survive cancer for many years, and applying the learning he found

Conscious Medicine, Gill Edwards. Piatkus, 2010. A synthesis of new understanding from physics and biology.

The World Within, Dr Patricia Worby. An exploration of the importance of our microbiome.

The Scar That Won't Heal: Stress, Trauma and Emotions in Chronic Disease, Dr Patricia Worby. An exploration of the biochemistry of trauma and stress, as well as some human software solutions.

A Doctor in the Wilderness, Dr Walter Yellowlees. A Scottish GP in the 1970s, this looks at how nutrition can affect health.

IPEA From Inner Peace Springs Effective Action
HWB, SWB Hardware body, Software Being
LYIS Love Your Immune System
VMN Vis Medicatrix Naturae – the healing power of nature
FEAR = False Evidence Appearing Real.
LWWBTL Life We Were Each Born To Live
LKS-CW Love and Kindness Supports - Criticism Withers
EDASD Every Day a School Day
EIMT Everyone is My Teacher
YRAYS You reap as you sow
WYPIIWYGO What You Put In Is What You Get Out
ULPL The Unwritten Lesson Plans of Life
TTTs Ten Top Tips
FINE Fearful, Insecure, Neurotic, Emotionally Imbalanced
6SP Six System Problems
NIH Not Invented Here (Give Up Your Thinking)
ISE Insecure Ego (Give Up Your Power)
MBS Mind-Body Split
ISQD Intuition Squashed
ATAC All Things are Connected (or not?)
TPOL The Paradox of Life
SSSCR Security Stimulation Support Control Responsiblity
WAGEF Where Attention Goes, Energy Flows
VRP Victim rescuer Persecutor (Drama Triangel)
TED The Empowerment Dynamic
GPP Games People Play (Eric Berne's book)
WDYYB Why Don't You Yes But from GPP
IWOTTHY I Was Only Trying to Help You from GPP
TFA The Five Agreements
BIWYW Be Impeccable with Your Word
TNP Take Nothing Personally
MNA Make No Assumptions
ADYB Always Do Your Best
BSLL Be Sceptical, but Learn to Listen
WGOBWGO What's Going On Behind What's Going On
LJL Life is a Journey of Learning
ERL Experience Reflect Learn
ERLRG, Experience, Reflect, Learn and Release, with Gratitude
ENAP Everyone Needs a Purpose
WYGOIWYGB The Law of Attraction says that what you give out is what you get back
WWRP What We Resist, Persists
ONA Observe, Not Absorb - don't be a sponge
RPRL Recognise Loss, Prevent Loss, Recover Loss, Let Go of Loss
SDAGBDA Shock Denial Anger Guilt Bargaining Depression Acceptance
HOPE – powerful medicine - hope!
ISSC Inner Smile Self Care
CrtlAltDelete resetting weather using the breath and finger acupressure
GYWR Give and You Will Receive
LCE Love Conquers Everything

05 Health and Self-Care

[1] www.fivewaystowellbeing.org

[2] Oschman, J. Energy Medicine. 2nd Ed. Elsevier, 2015.

[3] Tresidder, A. Vibrational Medicine, Allopathic medicine, Flower Essence Use and Paradigm Problems in Health Care. Int J Integr Med, Intech Open, 2013. http://bit.ly/HaSC002

[4] www.drmyhill.co.uk

06 Doctors as Patients

[1] Henderson M, Brooks SK, del Busso L, et al. Shame! Self-stigmatisation as an obstacle to sick doctors returning to work: a qualitative study. BMJ Open 2012;2(5).

[2] Curtis L. Unit costs of health and social care 2012. Secondary Unit costs of health and social care 2012 2012. www.pssru.ac.uk.

[3] Myers M, Gabbard G. The Physician as Patient. American Psychiatric Publishing, 2008.

[4] National mental health survey of doctors and students. Secondary National mental health survey of doctors and students 2013. http://bit.ly/HaSC003

[5] DH. Mental health and ill health in doctors. London: Department of Health, 2008.

[6] Schernhammer E, Colditz G. Suicide rates among physicians: a quantitative and gender assessment (meta-analysis). Am J Psychiatry 2004;161:2295-302.

[7] Kay M, Mitchell G, Clavarino A, et al. Doctors as patients: a systematic review of doctors' health access and the barriers they experience. [Review] [55 refs]. British Journal of General Practice 2008;58(552): 501-08.

[8] Brooks S, Gerada C, Chalder T. Doctors and dentists with mental ill health and addictions: outcomes of treatment from the Practitioner Health Programme. J Mental Health 2013;22:237-45.

[9] Garelick AI. Doctors' health: stigma and the professional discomfort in seeking help. The Psychiatrist 2012;36(3):81-84.

[10] Wessely A, Gerada C. When doctors need treatment: an anthropological approach to why doctors make bad patients. BMJ Careers 2013.

[11] GMC. Good Medical Practice. London: General Medical Council, 2012.

[12] BMA. Ethical responsibilities in treating doctors who are patients: British Medical Association, 2010.

08 Six System Problems

[1] "Men are not prisoners of fate, but prisoners of their own mind" is attributed to Franklin D Roosevelt.

[2] Romans 12:2, New King James Bible. Thomas Nelson, 2017

[3] Byrne E. Games People Play: The Psychology of Human Relationships. Grove Press, 1964. [Transactional Analysis; see section 05]

[4] Tresidder, A. Vibrational Medicine, Allopathic Medicine, Flower Essence Use and Paradigms and Challenges in Healthcare. Int J Integr Med, 2013, 1:29. doi: 10.5772/56864 http://bit.ly/HaSC002

[5] Rowling, JK. Harry Potter and the Chamber of Secrets, P333. Bloomsbury Publishing PLC, 1998.

[6] Shlain, L [neurosurgeon]. The Alphabet versus the Goddess: The Conflict Between Word And Image. Penguin, 1999.

[7] Oschman, J. Energy Medicine. 2nd Ed. Elsevier, 2015.

[8] Bolte-Taylor, J. My Stroke of Insight. Plume, 2008.

[9] Elmiger, J. Rediscovering Real Medicine: The New Horizons of Homeopathy. Element, 1998.

[10] Banks, S. The Enlightened Gardener. Vancouver: Lone Pine Publishing, 2001.

09 Self-Care and Physical Health

[1] Science of the Heart: Exploring the Role of the Heart in Human Performance. HeartMath Institute, 2017. http://bit.ly/HaSC004

[2] Deming, W Edwards. Out of the Crisis. MIT Press 2000.

[3] Lazarus, R PhD and Folkman, S PhD. Stress, Appraisal and Coping. Springer Publishing, 1984.

[4] Worby, Dr P. The Scar that Won't Heal: Stress, Trauma and Unresolved Emotion in Chronic Disease. Createspace Independent Publishing Platform, 2015.

[5] Mackarness, Dr R. Not All in the Mind. London: Pan, 1976.

[6] http://bit.ly/HaSC005

[7] www.powerwatch.org.uk

[8] Concise Oxford English Dictionary. Oxford University Press, 1964

[9] Wiley, TS with Formby, B Ph.D. Lights Out: Sleep, Sugar and Survival. Pocket Books, 2000.

[10] Includes Association of Anaesthetists resources on Fatigue: http://bit.ly/HaSC006

[11] http://bit.ly/HaSC007

[12] http://bit.ly/HaSC008

[13] http://bit.ly/HaSC009

[14] Oschman, J. Energy Medicine. 2nd Ed. Elsevier, 2015.

[15] http://bit.ly/HaSC010

[16] http://bit.ly/HaSC011

[17] www.electric-fields.com (Prof Denis Henshaw, Physics, Bristol); http://phiremedical.org
http://youtu.be/sNFdZVeXw7M (Dr Mallery-Blythe);
http://bit.ly/HaSC012 www.es-uk.info
www.electricsense.com www.powerwatch.org.uk
http://www.radiationresearch.org http://bit.ly/HaSC013 (The Ecologist)

10 Nutrition

[1] Myhill, S and Robinson, C. Prevent and Cure Diabetes: Delicious Diets, Not Dangerous Drugs. Hammersmith Health Books, 2016.

13 Interpersonal Energy flows

[1] Mesich, K. The Strength of Sensitivity. Llewellyn Publications, 2016.

14 Relationships 2: The Drama Triangle

[1] Byrne E. Games People Play: The Psychology of Human Relationships. Grove Press, 1964.

[2] George Bernard Shaw *in* The Doctor's Dilemma. Dir. Anthony Asquith, 1958.

[3] Karpman developed by Edwards, Karpman, S. Fairy tales and script drama analysis. 1968. http://bit.ly/HaSC014
Edwards, G. Conscious Medicine, pp130-133. Piatkus, 2010.

15 The Drama Triangle: Gill's Insights

[1] Edwards, G, July 2007. *Used for health teaching purposes with permission from 2010.*

16 Games That Get Played

Byrne E. Games People Play: The Psychology of Human Relationships. Grove Press, 1964.

de Board, R. Counselling for Toads, A Psychological Adventure. Routledge, 1998.

Kipling, R. Plain Tales from the Hills. 1888.

17 Relationships 3: The Five Agreements

[1] Ruiz, D M. The Four Agreements. San Rafael: Amber-Allen Publishing, 1997.
Ruiz, D M and Ruiz, D J. The Fifth Agreement, by Don Miguel Ruiz and Don Jose Ruiz. San Rafael: Amber-Allen Publishing, 2010.

[2] Watkins, A. Coherence, The Secret Science of Brilliant Leadership. Kogan Page, 2014.

19 How Life Works

[1] Davies, W H. Songs Of Joy and Others; Leisure. A. C. Fifield, 1911.

[2] *Based on* Matthew 15:11, New King James Bible. Thomas Nelson, 2017

[3] The official response from the Viktor Frankl institute is that it is not necessarily attributed to him. http://bit.ly/HaSC015
[4] Singer, M. The Untethered Soul. 2007, New Harbinger Publications, 2007.
[5] Alexander Pope (1688-1744) An Essay on Criticism, Part II (1711)
[6] Bach, E. Free Thyself *in* Collected Writings of Edward Bach, Flower Remedy Programme. Hereford, 1987.
[7] Banks, S. The Enlightened Gardener. Vancouver: Lone Pine Publishing, 2001.
[8] Sartori Dr P (PhD). The Wisdom of Near Death Experiences. Watkins Publishing Limited, 2014.
[9] Moody, R. Life after Life. Ebury Publishing , Rider & Co, 2001.
[10] Tibetan Book of the Dead
[11] int.michaelroads.org, by kind permission, first in Fountain Magazine, 2017.
[12] Currivan, J. The Cosmic Hologram: In-formation at the Centre of the Universe from a Physicist and scientist. Inner Traditions, 2017.

20 Emotional Self-Care

[1] Gleick, J. Chaos: Making a New Science. Penguin, 20th Anniversary Edition, 2008.
[2] http://emotionalchaostheory.blogspot.co.uk/ February 2010. Last accessed 30th June 2017.
[3] www.emotionallogiccentre.org.uk
[4] Damasio, A.R. Descartes' Error: Emotion, Reason and the Human Brain. Papermac, 1996.

21 Avoiding Desperation

[1] www.connectingwithpeople.org/resources
[2] http://www.nhs.uk/Conditions/Suicide/Pages/Introduction.aspx
[3] https://www.bma.org.uk/advice/work-life-support/your-wellbeing
http://bit.ly/HaSC016 (BMA Counselling and Doctor Advisor Service)
http://bit.ly/HaSC017 (support4doctors)
http://www.dsn.org.uk (Doctors Support Network, including for mental health issues)
http://php.nhs.uk (London Based Practitioner Health Programme)
http://www.rmbf.org (Royal Medical Benevolent Fund)
http://bit.ly/HaSC018 (Suicide prevention toolkit for employers)
http://bit.ly/HaSC019 (Suicide postvention: Crisis Management in the Event of a Suicide. A guide for Employers.)
https://www.mind.org.uk/workplace/ http://bit.ly/HaSC020
http://bit.ly/HaSC021 (MIND Wellness Action Plans at Work)
[4] http://bit.ly/HaSC022 (7 Key Questions)
[5] http://www.mensdevelopmentnetwork.ie

22 Knowing Yourself

[1] (Prof of Behavioural Science, Newcastle)

[2] Homeopathic Psychology, Philip M Bailey (1995)

[3] Briggs Myers, I and Briggs, K. Gifts Differing: Understanding Personality Type. Davies-Black, 1995.

[4] http://bit.ly/HaSC023/ (Myers-Briggs Type Indicators)

[5] Peter Honey, P and Mumford, A. The Manual of Learning Styles. Peter Honey Publications, 1986, 1992.

[6] www.businessballs.com

[7] Bach, Dr E. The Twelve Healers. CW Daniel, 1933.

24 Caring for the Whole Person

[1] Remodelling Medicine. Saltire Books, 2012.

[2] leaflets@rcpsych.ac.uk

[3] Powell, A. 'Soul-centred psychotherapy' www.rcpsych.ac.uk/powellarchive.

[4] Polkinghorne, J. Theology in the Context of Science. London: SPCK, 2008.

[5] Israel, M. The Intermediate Dimension. London: The Churches Fellowship for Psychical and Spiritual Studies, 1970.

[6] Sister Jane, SLG. Loving God Whatever. Harlech: Cairns Publications, 2006.

[7] Farrer, A. Law and Spirit. In Saving Belief. (Ed. Howatch, S.) London: Mowbray; Harrisburg: Morehouse Publishing.

25 Medical Mindfulness

[1] Adan, A. Cognitive performance and dehydration. Journal of the American College of Nutrition, 31(2), 71-78. 2012.

[2] Andrews-Hanna, J., Smallwood, J. & Spreng, R. The default network and self-generated thought Annals of the New York Academy of Sciences, 1316, 29-52. 2014.

[3] Oxford Mindfulness Centre, 2016. http://bit.ly/HaSC024

[4] Williams, M. & Penman, D. Mindfulness, a practical guide to finding peace in a frantic world. Piatkus, 2011.

[5] DeLosAngeles, D, Williams, G, and Burston, J. et al. Electroencephalographic correlates of states of concentrative meditation. International Journal of Psychophysiology, 110, 27-39. 2016.

[6] Hanson, R. 2014. http://bit.ly/HaSC025

[7] Khoury, B, Sharma, M, and Rush, S, et al. Mindfulness-based stress reduction for healthy individuals: A meta-analysis. Journal of Psychosomatic Research, 78(6), 519-28. 2015.

[8] Gotink, R, Chu, P, and Busschbach, J, et al. Standardised Mindfulness-

Based Interventions in Healthcare: An Overview of Systematic Reviews and Meta-Analyses of RCTs. PLoS One. 10(4), e0124344. 2015. http://bit.ly/HaSC026

[9] Krasner, M, Epstein, R, and Beckman, H, et al. Association of an educational program in mindful communication with burnout, empathy, and attitudes among primary care physicians, JAMA, 302(12). 1284-1293. 2009.

[10] Lutz, J, Herwiq, U, and Opialla, S, et al. Mindfulness and emotion regulation - an fMRI study. Social, Cognitive and Affective Neuroscience, 9(6), 776-785. 2014.

26 Changing Weather Fast

Lambrou, P and Pratt, G. Instant Emotional Healing: Acupressure for the Emotions. Broadway Books, 2006

Oschman, J. Energy Medicine. 2nd Ed. Elsevier, 2015.

27 Flower Essence use for Personal Development

[1] Romany poem, Kirk Yetholm

[2] Gurney, D F. A Little Book of Quiet; 'Gods Garden'. Country Life, 1915.

[3] www.edwardbach.org

[4] http://bit.ly/HaSC027 (Healing Herbs Direct Pocket Prescriber)

[5] Boog, G G. Energize Sua Empresa! Como os Florais Podem Dinamizar Seu Ambiente de Negócios. [Energize Your Company! How Flower Essences Can Enhance Your Business Performance.] People, 1997.

[6] *Books include*: many by Dr Bach (The Twelve Healers, and Heal Thyself) Judy Howard and Stefan Ball, Julian Barnard (especially The Essence Within, The Healing Herbs of Edward Bach), Mechthild Scheffer (Bach Flower Therapy and The Encyclopedia of Bach Flower Therapy), Clare G Harvey, Andrew Tresidder, Vivien Williamson (Bach Remedies and other Flower Essences), Philip Salmon and Anna Jeoffroy (Dr Bach Flower Remedies and the Chakras), Arthur Bailey (Bailey Flower Remedies), Rachel Singleton (Alight Within), Ian White (Bush Flower Essences), Kaminski and Katz (Flower Essence Repertory), Lila Devi (Essential Flower Essence Handbook) http://bit.ly/HaSC028

Vibrational Medicine, Allopathic Medicine, Flower Essence Use and Paradigms and Challenges in Healthcare by Dr Andrew Tresidder, http://bit.ly/HaSC029

Drops from Nature 7 minutes of joy, exploring how flower essences can help us. Filmed by Charles Wood, and interview by Rebecca Pow https://www.youtube.com/watch?v=5WpxH2jJsH4

30 Compassion in Healthcare 2

Gilbert, P. Compassion. Constable, 2009.

[1] Robin Philipp, R et al. Unpublished communication.
[2] de Zulueta, Dr P. Developing Compassionate Leadership in Health Care: an Integrative Review. 2015.
[3] Baverstock A. and Finlay F. Maintaining Compassion and Preventing Compassion Fatigue: A Practical Guide Arch Dis Child Ed Pract Ed. 2015.
[4] Pink, D H. Drive. New York: Riverhead Books, 2009.

31 Top Tips for Team Working for Senior Doctors

[1] Gawande , A. The Checklist Manifesto: How to Get Things Right. Profile Books Ltd, 2011.
[2] Covey, S. The 7 Habits of Highly Effective People. Simon and Schuster, 2004.

32 Emotional Health Strategy

[1] parentingcounts.org

Professional Support - please check with your professional body

Doctor's Support (UK Specific)
BMA Help Pages http://bit.ly/HaSC030
Doctors' Support Network
Royal Medical Benevolent Fund
Cameron Fund
DOCHelp
Doctors in Training: Deanery Support
Hospital Doctors: your employer and Wellness Programme, also Occupational Health
Hospital Doctors: your College - find out what support there is - you may find someone who needs it
GPs: your LMC and pastoral Support, GP Health www.gphealth.nhs.uk
Family and friends
MIND
The Samaritans 116123
Doctors in London: Practitioner Health Programme www.php.nhs.uk

Should you ever for any reason feel desperate, possibly even suicidal - please please share this with someone and ensure you get appropriate help. Suicidal crisis is a temporary state and will pass - especially if you are able to access help.

Problem: Clever minds out of balance may rationalize their feelings, and come to logical (but FALSE) conclusions that lead them into courses of action that for anyone else they would say 'Let me help you get better' - but for themselves fail to see the need for help.

Dr. Robin Philipp, FRCP, FRACP, FFOM, FFPHM, FNZCPHM, MSc(MedSc), DCH. Director, Centre for Health in Employment & the Environment, and Honorary Consultant Occupational and Public Health Physician,University Hospitals Bristol NHS Trust.

Dr Fiona Hayes MBBS MRCGP. GP specialising in Student Health, contributed towards GMC guidance on supporting medical students with mental health problems. Educator and facilitator in communication skills teaching. GP appraiser.

Dr Matthew Ridd is a GP in Portishead and Senior Lecturer at the Centre for Academic Primary Care, University of Bristol.

Prof Olaf G Aasland, Research Institute of the Norwegian Medical Association.

Dr. Paul Heaton BM DCH MRCP(UK) FRCPCH. In 1973 Paul's first encounter with paediatrics was as a research assistant at the Whittington Hospital in London. Since then he has worked as paediatrician at hospitals in New Zealand, London, and since 2002 at Yeovil.

Dr Patricia Saintey MB BS MRCGP LFHom DFSRH DipSIM. GP and Speciality Doctor of Integrative Medicine, including Heart Math Institute Heart Rate Variability assessment.

Lyn Page Certified Coach - ACC (ICF) and EIA Practitioner (EMCC). HeartMath Certified Coach and Licensed Trainer.

Dr Zoe Fox, B Med Sci (Hons), BM BS. Somerset GP, Transformational Coach, Facilitator and Faculty Member NHS Sustainable Improvement Team.

Gill Edwards, former NHS Psychologist, was a great teacher, mystic and author of many books including Living Magically, and Conscious Medicine.

Alex Aylward is an Organisational Coach, Mentor and Business Consultant.

Dr Trevor Griffiths, MA(Oxon), MBBS, MRCGP. Early-retired GP. Founder of the Emotional Logic Centre, training trainers internationally for primary mental health promotion by emotional literacy in schools, healthcare and businesses.

Dr Wiliam Bloom, PhD, author and educator, and founder/director of the Spiritual Companions Trust an educational charity that takes a holistic and person-centred approach to spirituality and wellness.

Revd Dr Jeremy Swayne, BM BCh, MRCGP, FFHom; retired GP and Homeopathic Physician; past Dean, Faculty of Homeopathy; C of E priest, Diocese of Bath and Wells.

Dr Maya Roberts, MRCPsych, former Consultant Psychiatrist and Mindfulness